Karen

The African Child

Camara Laye was born in Guinea in 1924.
A child of intellectual promise, he went
first to the technical college at Conakry,
the capital of Guinea, and later to France
to study engineering. In Paris he found a
totally different culture and, lonely and
unhappy, wrote his first book, *The African
Child*.

This largely autobiographical work tells
the story of his childhood among the Malinke tribe, surrounded by ritual magic and
superstition, and his emergence into manhood and independence.

Twelve years later, having returned to his
native land, Camara Laye wrote *A Dream
of Africa*. In this sequel to *The African
Child*, the narrator—now influenced by his
experiences in Europe—sees an Africa on
the violent brink of independence.

Fontana African Fiction

The African Child

Camara Laye

Translated by James Kirkup

Introduction by William Plomer

Fontana/Collins

First published in French under the title
L'Enfant Noir by Librarie Plon in 1954
First published in English under the title
The Dark Child 1955
First published in Fontana Books 1959
Thirty-seventh Impression October 1982

© Camara Laye 1954

Made and printed in Great Britain by
William Collins Sons & Co. Ltd, Glasgow

TO MY MOTHER

Black woman, woman of Africa, O my mother, I am thinking of you . . .

O Daman. O my mother, you who bore me upon your back, you who gave me suck, you who watched over my first faltering steps, you who were the first to open my eyes to the wonders of the earth, I am thinking of you . . .

Woman of the fields, woman of the rivers, woman of the great river-banks, O you my mother, I am thinking of you . . .

O you, Daman, O my mother, you who dried my tears, you who filled my heart with laughter, you who patiently bore with all my many moods, how I should love to be beside you once again, to be a little child beside you!

Woman of great simplicity, woman of great resignation, O my mother I am thinking of you . . .

O Daman. Daman, you of the great family of black-smiths and goldsmiths, my thoughts are always turning towards you, and your own thoughts accompany me at every step. O Daman, my mother, how I should love to be surrounded by your loving warmth again, to be a little child beside you . . .

Black woman, woman of Africa, O my mother, let me thank you; thank you for all that you have done for me, your son, who, though so far away, is still so close to you!

INTRODUCTION

IN FRENCH GUINEA, where the Niger flows northward and eastward to Timbuktu, away from the Atlantic into which its waters will pour at last, live the Malinke. They live behind and beyond Sierra Leone and Liberia, a still mainly agrarian people whose culture has evidently harmonised Islamic and ancient African traditions. A son of Malinke, whose natural ability and enterprise have enabled him to benefit by a French education, has now made a name for himself by writing a book about his childhood and youth. Camara Laye's book is something rare and valuable. Not all the patience, curiosity, resolution, and ferretings of the most accomplished anthropologist could have elicited these particular facts. Memory chose them. Taste arranged them. One human heart has given them life and warmth. The result is a work of art—and a work of art, if not a miracle, always appears miraculous.

It is not an earthly paradise to which Camara Laye introduces us, but a coherent society with a consistent manner of life which appears entirely free from vulgarity. It is a formal society permeated by a sense of mystery. No attempt is made to explain everything. Experience elsewhere shows that to do so often means explaining everything *away*. "Are there not things everywhere around us," he asks, "that are incapable of explanation?" Where he grew up the sense of community is implicit and inherent. Tradition and long usage have created politeness, correctness, mutual respect, and simple dignity, but the ceremoniousness of life is not rigid or a matter of empty or elaborate forms. In work or in play (the line between which is not easily to be drawn and need not be drawn) nothing

7

is cheapened, everything is given its due importance: the making of a trinket, etiquette at meal times, the harvesting of the rice, the rites of initiation into manhood, are communal acts in which the individual exerts his best scope or skill, because he has never a doubt that he belongs to what is going on and is a necessary part of it.

Autobiography is best without self-pity, self-justification, or boastfulness. *The African Child* is quite without these weaknesses. Clear, fresh, direct, it seems to combine the kind of lucidity that can easily be called French with a warmth that is unmistakably African. As a picture of a young African's discovery of the world about him it is likely to be unforgettable. Camara Laye's unfolding of his various feelings about his kinsfolk and friends and of their behaviour is affectionate and skilful at the same time, and the delicate precision with which he describes his love for Marie crystallises a not uncommon but not easily definable phase in the emotional development of the human male. But perhaps it is in the noble portraits of his father and mother that Camara Laye will most touch the European reader: the final interview with them before his departure for remote and unknown Argenteuil is wonderful in its imaginative understanding of their feelings as well as in its natural rendering of his own.

This in some ways deceptively simple story is the work of a "dark child" uncorrupted by the complexity and dislocation of the world we know. The anxiety aroused in the reader lest so candid a nature should be perhaps smeared or injured by the stain of being "displaced" in an alien Europe is a measure of the sympathetic interest created by what he had to say and the way he has said it.

The book has repeatedly put me in mind of Yeats's lines:

> *How but in custom and in ceremony*
> *Are innocence and beauty born?*

It has fittingly been translated into English by a poet capable of responding to Camara Laye's evocations of the universal in the particular.

WILLIAM PLOMER.

One

I WAS a little boy playing round my father's hut. How old would I have been at that time? I cannot remember exactly. I still must have been very young: five, maybe six years old. My mother was in the workshop with my father, and I could just hear their familiar voices above the noise of the anvil and the conversation of the customers.

Suddenly I stopped playing, my whole attention fixed on a snake that was creeping round the hut. He really seemed to be 'taking a turn' round the hut. After a moment I went over to him. I had taken in my hand a reed that was lying in the yard – there were always some lying around; they used to get broken off the fence of plaited reeds that marked the boundary of our compound – and I thrust this reed into the reptile's mouth. The snake did not try to get away: he was beginning to enjoy our little game; he was slowly swallowing the reed; he was devouring it, I thought, as if it were some delicious prey, his eyes glittering with voluptuous bliss; and inch by inch his head was drawing nearer to my hand. At last the reed was almost entirely swallowed up, and the snake's jaws were terribly close to my fingers.

I was laughing, I had not the slightest fear, and now I know that the snake would not have hesitated much longer before burying his fangs in my fingers if, at that moment, Damany, one of the apprentices, had not come out of the workshop. The apprentice shouted to my father, and almost at once I felt myself lifted off my feet: I was safe in the arms of one of my father's friends!

There was a terrific commotion going on all round

me; my mother was shouting harder than anyone; and she gave me a few sharp slaps. I began to weep, more upset by the sudden uproar than by the blows I had received. A little later, when I had calmed down a little and the shouting had died down around me, my mother solemnly warned me never to play such a game again; and I promised, although I could not really see where the danger in it lay.

My father's hut was near the workshop, and I would often play there beneath the veranda that ran round the outside. It was my father's private hut. It was built like all our huts, of mud that had been pounded and moulded into bricks with water; it was round, and proudly helmeted with thatch. It was entered by a rectangular doorway. Inside, a tiny window let in a thin shaft of daylight. On the right there was the bed, made of beaten earth like the bricks, spread with a simple wicker-work mat on which was a pillow stuffed with kapok. At the rear of the hut, right under the window where the light was strongest, were the tool-boxes. On the left were the *boubous* and the prayer-rugs. Finally, at the head of the bed, hanging over the pillow and watching over my father's slumber, there was a series of pots that contained extracts from plants and the bark of trees. These pots all had metal lids and they were profusely and curiously garlanded with chaplets of cowrie shells; it did not take me long to discover that they were the most important things in the hut: they contained the magic charms, those mysterious liquids that keep evil spirits at bay, and, smeared on the body, make it invulnerable to black magic, to all kinds of black magic. My father, before he went to bed, never failed to smear his body with a little of each liquid, first one, then another, for each charm had its own particular property: but exactly *what* property I do not know: I left my father's house too soon.

From the veranda under which I played I could keep an eye on the workshop opposite, and they for their part could keep an eye on me. This workshop was the main building in our compound. That is where my father was generally to be found, supervising the work, forging the most important items himself, or repairing delicate mechanisms; here it was that he received his friends and his customers, so that the place resounded with noise from morning to night. Moreover, everyone entering or leaving our compound had to pass through the workshop, so that there was a perpetual coming and going, though no one ever seemed to be in a hurry : each one would pause to have a word with my father and spend a few moments watching the work in hand. Sometimes I would draw near the door, but I rarely went in, for everyone used to frighten me there, and I would run away as soon as anyone tried to lay hands on me. It was not until very much later that I got into the habit of crouching in a corner of the workshop and watching the fire blazing in the forge.

My private domain at that time consisted of the veranda that ran round the outside of my father's hut; and the orange tree that grew in the middle of the compound.

As soon as you had crossed the workshop and gone through the door at the back, you could see the orange tree. If I compare it with the giants of our native forests, the tree was not very big, but its mass of glossy leaves used to cast a dense shadow that was a cool refuge from the blazing sun. When it was in flower, a heady perfume was wafted over the entire compound. When the fruit appeared, we were allowed only to look : we had to possess our souls in patience until they were ripe. Then my father, who, as head of the family – a family of innumerable members – governed the compound, would give the order to pick them. The men who did the picking brought their baskets one by one to my father, who shared them out among the inhabitants of the compound, his neighbours and his customers; after that we were permitted to help ourselves from the baskets, as much as we liked! My father was an open-handed and, in fact, a lavish giver; no matter who turned up, he would share our meals; and as I could never keep up with the speed at which such guests used to eat, I might have remained everlastingly hungry if my mother had not taken the precaution of putting my share on one side.

'Sit here,' she would say, 'and eat, for your father's crazy.'

She did not look upon such guests with too kindly an eye; there were too many of them for her liking, all bent on filling their bellies at her expense. My father, for his part, ate very sparingly: he was a very abstemious man.

We lived near the railway track. The trains travelled along outside the fence of plaited reeds which marked the confines of our compound; in fact they ran so close to it that sparks from the engines would sometimes set fire to the palisade, and we all would have to rush to put it out at once, if we did not want to see the whole thing go up in flames. These alarms, rather frightening, but rather exciting too, made me watch every train that went by; and even when there was not a train in sight – for at that time the traffic on the railroad depended entirely on the river traffic, which was very irregular – I would go and spend long periods just looking at the gleaming metal rails. They always glittered cruelly under the fierce sun, for at this point there was no foliage to diminish its intensity. Baked by the sun from early morning the ballast of red stone was burningly hot: so hot in fact that the oil which fell from the engines was immediately evaporated, leaving not the slightest trace. Was it this oven-like warmth or the oil, the inescapable

smell of the oil, which attracted the snakes? I do not
know. The fact is that I often came across snakes crawling over the sun-baked ballast; and inevitably the snakes
used to creep into the compound.

Ever since the day I had been forbidden to play with
snakes, I would run to my mother as soon as I saw one.

'There's a snake!' I would cry.

'What, another?' my mother would shout.

And she would come running out to see what sort of
a snake it was. If it was just a snake like any other
snake – actually, they were all quite different! – she
would beat it to death at once; and, like all the women
of our country, she would work herself up into a frenzy,
beating the snake to a pulp, whereas the men would content themselves with a single hard blow, neatly struck.

One day, however, I noticed a little black snake with
a strikingly marked body that was proceeding leisurely
in the direction of the workshop. I ran to warn my
mother, as usual. But as soon as my mother saw the
black snake she said to me gravely:

'My son, this one must not be killed: he is not as
other snakes, and he will not harm you; you must never
interfere with him.'

Everyone in our compound knew that this snake must
not be killed; excepting myself, and, I suppose, my little
playmates, who were still just ignorant children.

'This snake,' my mother added, 'is your father's
guiding spirit.'

I gazed dumbfounded at the little snake. He was proceeding calmly towards the workshop; he was moving
gracefully, very sure of himself, and almost as if conscious
of his immunity; his body, black and brilliant, glittered
in the harsh light of the sun. When he reached the
workshop, I noticed for the first time, cut out level with
the ground, a small hole in the wall. The snake disappeared through this hole.

'Look,' said my mother, 'the serpent is going to pay your father a visit.'

Although I was familiar with the supernatural, this sight filled me with such astonishment that I was struck dumb. What business would a snake have with my father? And why this particular snake? No one had to kill him, because he was my father's guiding spirit! At any rate, that was the explanation my mother had given me. But what exactly *was* a 'guiding spirit'? What were these guiding spirits that I encountered almost everywhere, forbidding one thing, commanding another to be done? I could not understand it at all, though their presences were around me as I grew to manhood. There were good spirits, and there were evil ones; and more evil than good ones, it seemed to me. And how was I to know that this snake was harmless? It looked the same as any other snake; it was, of course, a *black* snake, and certainly there was something unusual about it; but after all, it *was* only a snake! I was absolutely baffled, but I did not ask my mother about it: I felt I would have to ask my father himself about it, almost as if this mystery was something in which women could have no part; it was a mysterious affair that could only be discussed with men. I decided to wait until nightfall.

Immediately after the evening meal, when the palavers were over, my father bade his friends farewell and went to sit under the veranda of his hut; I went and sat near him. I began questioning him in a roundabout manner, as all children do, and on every subject under the sun. Finally, unable to restrain myself any longer, I asked:

'My father, what is that little snake that comes to visit you?'

'What snake do you mean?'

'Why, the little black snake that my mother forbids us to kill.'

'Ah!' he said.

He gazed at me for a long while. He seemed to be considering whether to answer or not. Perhaps he was thinking about how old I was, perhaps he was wondering if it was not a little too soon to confide such a secret to a twelve-year-old boy. Then suddenly he made up his mind.

'That snake,' he said, 'is the guiding spirit of our race. Can you understand that?'

'Yes,' I answered, although I did not understand very well.

'That snake,' he went on, 'has always been with us; he has always made himself known to one of us. In our time, it is to me that he has made himself known.'

'That is true,' I said.

And I said it with all my heart, for it seemed obvious to me that the snake could have made himself known to no one but my father. Was not my father the head man in our compound? Was it not my father who had authority over all the blacksmiths in our district? Was he not the most skilled? Was he not, after all, my father?

'How did he make himself known?' I asked.

'First of all, he made himself known in the semblance of a dream. He appeared to me several times in slumber, and he told me the day on which he would appear to me in reality: he gave me the precise time and place. But when I really saw him for the first time, I was filled with fear. I took him for a snake like any other snake, and I had to keep myself in control, or I would have tried to kill him. When he saw that I did not receive him kindly, he turned away and departed the way he had come. And there I stood watching him depart, and wondering all the time if I should not simply have killed him there and then; but a power greater than myself stayed my hand and prevented me from pursuing him. I stood watching him disappear. And even then, at that very moment, I could easily have overtaken him; a few swift strides would have been enough; but I was struck motionless by a kind of paralysis. Such was my first encounter with the little black snake.'

He was silent a moment, then went on :

'The following night, I saw the snake again in my dream. "I came as I foretold," he said, "but thou didst not receive me kindly; nay, rather I did perceive that thou didst intend to receive me unkindly : I did read it thus in thine eyes. Wherefore dost thou reject me? Lo, I am the guiding spirit of thy race, and it is even as the guiding spirit of thy race that I make myself known to thee, as to the most worthy. Therefore forbear to look with fear upon me, and beware that thou dost not reject me, for behold, I bring thee good fortune." After that, I received the serpent kindly when he made himself known to me a second time; I received him without fear, I received him with loving kindness, and he has brought me nothing but good.'

My father again was silent for a moment, then he said :

'You can see for yourself that I am not more gifted than any other man, that I have nothing which other men have not also, and even that I have less than others, since I give everything away, and would even give away the last thing I had, the shirt on my back. Nevertheless, I am better known than other men, and my name is on everyone's tongue, and it is I who have authority over all the blacksmiths in the five cantons. If these things are so, it is by virtue of this snake alone, who is the guiding spirit of our race. It is to this snake that I owe everything, and it is he likewise who gives me warning of all that is to happen. Thus I am never surprised, when I awake, to see this or that person waiting for me outside my workshop: I already know that he or she will be there. No more am I surprised when this or that motor bicycle or bicycle breaks down, or when an accident happens to a clock: because I had foreknowledge of what would come to pass. Everything is transmitted to me in the course of the night, together with an account of all the work I shall have to perform, so that from the start, without having to cast about in my mind, I know how to repair whatever is brought to me; and it is these things that have established my renown as a craftsman. But all this – let it never be forgotten – I owe to the snake, I owe it to the guiding spirit of our race.'

He was silent; and then I understood why, when my father used to come back from a walk he could enter the workshop and say to the apprentices: 'During my absence, this or that person has been here, he was dressed in such and such a way, he came from such and such a place and he brought with him such and such a piece of work to be done.' And all marvelled at this curious knowledge. Now I understood how my father obtained his information. When I raised my eyes, I saw that my father was watching me.

'I have told you all these things, little one, because you are my son, the eldest of my sons, and because I have nothing to hide from you. There is a certain form of behaviour to observe, and certain ways of acting in order that the guiding spirit of our race may approach you also. I, your father, was observing that form of behaviour which persuades our guiding spirit to visit us. Oh, perhaps not consciously. But nevertheless it is true that if you desire the guiding spirit of our race to visit you one day, if you desire to inherit it in your turn, you will have to conduct yourself in the selfsame manner; from now on, it will be necessary for you to be more and more in my company.'

He gazed at me with burning eyes, then suddenly he heaved a sigh.

'I fear, I very much fear, little one, that you are not often enough in my company. You are all day at school, and one day you shall depart from that school for a greater one. You will leave me, little one . . .'

And again he heaved a sigh. I saw that his heart was heavy within him. The hurricane-lamp hanging on the veranda cast a harsh glare on his face. He suddenly seemed to me like an old man.

'Father !' I cried.

'Son . . .' he whispered.

And I was no longer sure whether I ought to continue to attend the school or whether I ought to remain in the workshop : I felt unutterably confused.

'Go now,' said my father.

I got up and went to my mother's hut. The night was full of sparkling stars; an owl was hooting nearby. Ah, what was the right path for me? Did I know yet where that path lay? My perplexity was boundless as the sky, and mine was a sky, alas, without any stars . . . I entered my mother's hut, which at that time was mine also, and went to bed at once. But sleep evaded me, and I tossed restlessly on my bed.

'What's the matter with you?' asked my mother.

'Nothing.'

No, I couldn't find anything to say.

'Why don't you go to sleep?' went on my mother.

'I don't know.'

'Go to sleep !' she said.

'Yes,' I said.

'Sleep . . . Nothing can resist sleep,' she said sadly. Why did she, too, appear so sad? Had she divined my distress? Anything that concerned me she sensed very deeply. I was trying to sleep, but I shut my eyes and lay still in vain: the image of my father under the storm-lantern would not leave me. He had suddenly seemed so old, he who was so youthful, so active, more youthful and more active than any of us and who in the running of races never let himself be outstripped by anyone, whose limbs were swifter than the limbs of all our young men . . . 'Father! . . . Father! . . .' I kept repeating it. 'Father, what must I do, what is the right thing to do?' And I wept quietly, and weeping I fell asleep.

After that, we never mentioned the little black snake again: my father had spoken to me about him for the first and the last time. But from that time forth, as soon as I saw the little snake, I would run and sit in the workshop. I would watch him glide through the little hole in the wall. As if informed of his presence, my father at that instant would turn his eyes to the hole and give a smile. The snake would proceed straight towards him, opening his jaws. When he was within reach, my father would stroke him with his hand, and the snake would accept the caress with a quivering of his whole body: never did I see the little snake attempt to do the slightest harm to my father. That caress, and the answering tremor – but I ought to say: that appealing caress and that answering tremor – threw me each time into an inexpressible confusion: I would imagine I know not what mysterious conversation . . . the hand inquired, and the tremor replied . . .

Yes, it was like a conversation. Would I, too, converse like that one day? No: I was still attending the school. Yet I would have liked so much to place my hand, my own hand, on the snake, and to understand and listen to that tremor too; but I did not know how the snake would have taken my hand, and I felt now that he would have nothing to tell me; I was afraid that he would never have anything to tell me . . .

When my father felt that he had stroked the snake enough, he left him alone; then the snake would coil himself under the edge of one of the sheep-skins on which my father was seated, facing his anvil.

Two

OF ALL the different kinds of work my father performed, none fascinated me so much as his skill with gold. No other occupation was so noble, no other needed such a delicate touch; and, moreover, this sort of work was always a kind of festival : it was a real festival that broke the monotony of ordinary working days.

So if a woman, accompanied by a go-between, crossed the threshold of the workshop, I would follow her in at once. I knew what she wanted : she had brought some gold and wanted to ask my father to transform it into a trinket. The woman would have collected the gold in the placers of Siguiri, where, for months on end, she would have crouched over the river, washing the mud and patiently extracting from it the grains of gold. These women never came alone : they were well aware that my father had other things to do than to make trinkets for all and sundry ! and even if the making of jewellery had been his main occupation, they would have realised that they were not his first or his only customers, and that their wants could not be immediately attended to.

Generally these women required the trinket for a certain date, either for the festival of Ramadan or for the Tabaski; or for some other family festivity, or for a dance ceremony.

Thereupon, to better their chance of being quickly

served, and the more easily to persuade my father to interrupt the work he had in hand, they would request the services of an official praise-singer, a go-between, and would arrange with him in advance what fee they would pay for his good offices.

The praise-singer would install himself in the workshop, tune up his cora, which is our harp, and would begin to sing my father's praises. This was always a great event for me. I would hear recalled the lofty deeds of my father's ancestors, and the names of these ancestors from the earliest times; as the couplets were reeled off, it was like watching the growth of a great genealogical tree that spread its branches far and wide and flourished its boughs and twigs before my mind's eye. The harp played an accompaniment to this vast utterance of names, expanding it and punctuating it with notes that were now soft, now shrill. Where did the praise-singer get his information from? He must certainly have developed a very retentive memory stored with facts handed down to him by his predecessors, for this is the basis of all our oral traditions. Did he embellish the truth? It is very likely : flattery is the praise-singer's stock-in-trade! Nevertheless, he was not allowed to take too many liberties with tradition, for it is part of the praise-singer's task to preserve it. But in those days such considerations did not enter my head, which I would hold high and proud; for I used to feel quite drunk with so much praise, which seemed to reflect some of its effulgence upon my own small person.

I could tell that my father's vanity was being inflamed, and I already knew that after having sipped this milk-and-honey he would lend a favourable ear to the woman's request. But I was not alone in my knowledge; the woman also had seen my father's eyes gleaming with contented pride; and she would hold out her grains of gold as if the whole thing was settled : my father, taking up his scales, would weigh the gold.

'What sort of trinket do you desire?' he would ask.
'I want . . .'

And often it would happen that the woman did not
know really what she wanted, because she would be so
torn by desire, because she would have liked to have
many, many trinkets, all out of the same small quantity
of gold : but she would have had to have much more
than she had brought with her to satisfy such a desire,
and eventually she would have to content herself with
some more modest wish.

'When do you want it for?' my father would ask.

And she would always want it at once.

'Why are you in such a hurry? How do you expect
me to find the time?'

'It's very urgent, I can assure you,' the woman
would reply.

'That's what all women say, when they want an
ornament. Well, I'll see what I can do. Now are you
happy?'

Then he would take the clay pot that was kept specially
for the smelting of gold and pour in the grains; thereupon he would cover the gold with powdered charcoal,
a charcoal which he obtained by the use of plant juices
of exceptional purity; finally he would place a large
lump of the same kind of charcoal over the whole thing.

Then, having seen the work duly undertaken, the
woman, by now quite satisfied, would go back to her
household tasks, leaving her go-between to carry on with
the praise-singing which had already proved so advan-
tageous to her.

On a sign from my father, the apprentices would start
working the two pairs of sheep-skin bellows which were
placed on the ground at each side of the forge and linked
to it by earthen pipes. These apprentices remained seated
all the time, with crossed legs, in front of the bellows;

at least the younger did, for the elder would sometimes be allowed to take part in the craftsmen's work and the younger – in those days it was Sidafa – only had to work the bellows and watch the proceedings while awaiting his turn to be elevated to less rudimentary tasks. For a whole hour they would both be working the levers of the bellows till the fire in the forge leapt into flame, becoming a living thing, a lively and merciless spirit.

Then my father, using long pincers, would lift the clay pot and place it on the flames.

Immediately all work would more or less stop in the workshop : actually while the gold is being melted and while it is cooling all work with copper or aluminium is supposed to stop, for fear that some fraction of these less noble metals might fall among the gold. It is only steel that can still be worked at such times. But workmen who had some piece of steel work in hand would either hasten to finish it or would openly stop work to join the other apprentices gathered round the forge. In fact, there were often so many of them at these times pressing round my father that I, the smallest, would have to get up and push my way in among them, so as not to miss any of the operation.

It might happen that, feeling he had too little room to work in, my father would make his apprentices stand well away from him. He would merely raise his hand in a simple gesture : at that particular moment he would never utter a word, and no one else would, no one was allowed to utter a word, even the go-between's voice would no longer be raised in song; the silence would be broken only by the panting of the bellows and by the faint hissing of the gold. But if my father never used to utter actual words at this time, I know that he was uttering them in his mind; I could see it by his lips that kept working while he bent over the pot and kept stirring the gold and the charcoal with a bit of wood that would keep bursting into flame, and so had to be constantly replaced by a fresh bit.

What were the words my father's lips were forming? I do not know; I do not know for certain : I was never told what they were. But what else could they have been, if not magical incantations? Were they not the spirits of fire and gold, of fire and air, air breathed through the earthen pipes, of fire born of air, of gold married with fire – were not these the spirits he was invoking? Was it not their help and their friendship he was calling upon in this marriage of elemental things? Yes, it was almost certainly those spirits he was calling upon, for they are the most elemental of all spirits, and their presence is essential at the melting of the gold.

The operation that was going on before my eyes was simply the smelting of gold; but it was something more than that : a magical operation that the guiding spirits could look upon with favour or disfavour; and that is why there would be all round my father that absolute silence and that anxious expectancy. I could understand, though I was just a child, that there was no craft greater than the goldsmith's. I expected a ceremony, I had come to be present at a ceremony, and it really was one, though very protracted. I was still too young to be able to understand why it was so protracted; nevertheless, I had an inkling, beholding the almost religious concentration of all those present as they watched the mixing process.

When finally the gold began to melt, I used to feel like shouting, and perhaps we would all have shouted if we had not been forbidden to make a sound : I would be trembling, and certainly everyone else would be trembling as we sat watching my father stirring the mixture, still a heavy paste in which the charcoal was gradually being consumed. The next stage followed swiftly; the gold now had the fluidity of water. The guiding spirits had smiled on the operation!

'Bring me the brick!' my father would say, thus lifting the ban that until then had kept us all silent.

The brick, which an apprentice would place beside the fire, was hollowed out, generously greased with Galam butter. My father would take the pot off the fire, tilt it carefully, and I would watch the gold flowing into the brick, flowing like liquid fire. True, it was only a very sparse trickle of fire, but oh, how vivid, how brilliant! As the gold flowed into the brick, the grease would splutter and flame and give off a thick smoke that caught in the throat and stung the eyes, leaving us all weeping and coughing.

It occurred to me later on that my father could easily have relinquished all the work of smelting the gold to one or other of his assistants: they were not without experience in these matters, they had taken part hundreds of times in the same preparations and they would certainly have brought the work to a successful conclusion. But as I have told you, my father kept moving his lips! We could now hear those words, those secret words, those incantations which he addressed to powers that we should not, that we could not hear or see: this was essential. Only my father was versed in the science of conjuring the spirits of fire, air and gold, and conjuring evil spirits, and that is why he alone conducted the whole operation.

By now the gold would have cooled in the hollow of the brick, and my father would begin to hammer and stretch it. This was the moment when his work as a goldsmith really began. I noticed that before embarking on it he never failed to stroke stealthily the little snake coiled up under the sheep-skin; one can only assume that this was his way of gathering strength for what remained to be done, and which was the most difficult.

But was it not extraordinary, was it not miraculous

that on these occasions the little black serpent always coiled up under the sheep-skin? He was not always there, he did not visit my father every day, but he was always present whenever there was gold to be worked.

Moreover, it is our custom to keep apart from the working of gold all influences outside those of the jeweller himself. And indeed it is not precisely because the jeweller alone possesses the secret of his incantations; but also because the working of gold, besides being a task of the greatest skill, is a matter of confidence, of conscience, a task which is not undertaken excepting after due reflection and experiment. Finally, I do not think that any jeweller would renounce the opportunity of performing such a task – I ought to say, such a spectacle! – in which he can display his abilities with a virtuosity that his work as a blacksmith or a mechanic or even as a sculptor is never invested with; even though in these more humble tasks his skill is no less wonderful, even though the statues which he carves in wood with his adze are not insignificant works!

The snake's presence came as no surprise to me; ever since that evening when my father had talked to me about the guiding spirit of our race, it had ceased to surprise me; it was quite natural that the snake should be there: he had knowledge of the future. Did he impart any of that knowledge to my father? It seemed to me quite obvious that he did: did he not always warn him of what was going to happen? But I had another reason for believing implicitly in the powers of the little snake.

The craftsman who works in gold must first of all purify himself, that is, he must wash himself all over and, of course, abstain from all sexual relationships during the whole time. Great respecter of ceremony as he was, it would have been impossible for my father to ignore these rules. Now I never saw him make these preparations; I would see him address himself to his work without apparent preliminaries. But from that moment it was obvious that, forewarned by his black guiding spirit in a dream of the task that would await him in the morning, my father must have prepared for it as soon as he arose, and had entered his workshop in a state of purity, his body smeared with the magical substances hidden in his numerous pots full of secret potions. So I believe my father never entered his workshop except in a state of ritual purity; and that is not because I want to make him out as being better than he is — he is a man like any other, and has a man's weaknesses — but always when it was a matter of ritual he was uncompromisingly strict.

The woman for whom the trinket was being made, and who would often have looked in to see how the work was getting on, would come for the final time, not wanting to miss anything of the marvellous sight as the gold wire, which my father had succeeded in spinning, was transformed into a trinket. She was here now, devouring with her eyes the fragile golden wire, following its tranquil and inevitable spirals round the little metal cone which gave the trinket its shape. My father would be watching her out of the corner of his eye, and sometimes I would see the corners of his mouth twitch into a smile : the woman's avid attentiveness amused him.

'Are you trembling?' he would say to her.

'*Am* I trembling?' she would ask.

And we would all burst out laughing at her. For she *was* trembling! She was trembling with covetousness for the spiral pyramid in which my father was inserting, among the convolutions, tiny grains of gold. When finally he terminated the work by placing at the summit the largest grain of gold, the woman would jump excitedly to her feet.

Then, while my father was slowly turning the trinket round in his fingers, smoothing it into perfect shape, no one could have displayed such utter happiness as the native woman, not even the praise-singer, whose trade it was to do so, and who, during the whole process of transformation, had kept on singing his praises, accelerating his rhythm, increasing his flatteries as the trinket took shape, and praising my father's talents to the skies.

Indeed, the praise-singer participated in a curious — I was going to say direct, effective — way in the work. He, too, was intoxicated with the joy of creation; he declaimed his rapture, and plucked his harp like a man inspired; he warmed to the task as if he had been the craftsman himself, as if the trinket had been made by his own hands. He was no longer a paid thurifer; he was no longer just the man whose services each and anyone could hire : he had become a man who creates his song under the influence of some very personal, interior necessity.

When my father, after having soldered the large grain of gold that crowned the summit, held out his work to be admired, the go-between would no longer be able to contain himself, and would intone the douga — the great chant which is only sung for celebrated men, and which is danced to only for them.

But the douga is a tremendous chant, a provocative chant, a chant that the go-between would not venture to sing, and that the man for whom it is sung would not venture to dance, without certain precautions.

My father, forewarned in a dream, had been able to take these precautions as soon as he got up; the praise-singer had taken them as a matter of course when he had made his bargain with the woman. Just as my father had done, he had smeared his body with magic lotions and so had rendered himself invulnerable to the bad spirits which the douga would undoubtedly stir into activity, invulnerable also even to his fellow praise-singers who, jealous perhaps, were only waiting to hear the chant, the note of exaltation and the loss of control which that exaltation entails, to cast their evil spells upon him.

At the first notes of the douga, my father would rise and utter a cry in which happiness and triumph were equally mingled; and brandishing in his right hand the hammer that was the symbol of his profession, and in his left a ram's horn filled with magic substances, he would dance the glorious dance.

No sooner had he finished than workmen and apprentices, friends and customers in their turn, not forgetting the woman for whom the trinket had been created, would flock round him, congratulating him, showering praises on him, and complimenting at the same time the go-between, who found himself laden with gifts, gifts that are almost the only resources he has in his wandering life, that he leads after the fashion of the troubadours of old. Beaming, aglow with dancing and the praises he had received, my father would offer kola nuts, that small change of Guinean civility.

All that now remained to be done was to redden the trinket in a little water mixed with chlorine and sea-salt. I could go now: the ceremony was over! But often, as I was leaving the workshop, my mother, who might be in the yard pounding millet or rice, would call me.

'Where have you been?' she would ask, although she knew very well where I had been.

'In the workshop.'

'Oh, yes, your father was making something out of gold. Gold! It's always gold!'

And she would pound furiously the helpless bowl of rice or millet. 'Your father's ruining his health! You see what he's doing.'

'He's been dancing the douga,' I would reply.

'The douga! The douga won't stop him ruining

his eyesight! And you would be better off playing here in the yard instead of going and breathing the dust and smoke in the workshop!'

My mother did not like my father to work with gold. She knew how harmful the soldering of gold can be: a jeweller can wear his lungs out, puffing at his blow-pipe, and his eyes suffer by being so close to the intense heat of the forge; and even more perhaps from the microscopic delicacy of the work. But even if there had been no danger in it, my mother still would have dis-liked this sort of work: she held it in suspicion, for you cannot solder gold without the help of other metals, and my mother used to think that it was not strictly honest to keep the gold which was saved by its alloys, although this was the accepted thing; and she, too, was quite prepared, whenever she took cotton to be woven, to receive in return a piece of cloth of only half the original weight.

Three

I OFTEN used to go and spend a few days at Tindican, a small village to the west of Kouroussa. My mother was born at Tindican, and her mother and brothers still lived there. I was always highly delighted to be going there, for they were very fond of me, and my grand-mother in particular, for whom my visit was always a great treat, took great pleasure in petting me; and I for my part loved her with all my heart.

She was a tall woman, still with jet-black hair, slim, very erect, and strong; in fact, she was still fairly young and still did her share in the farm work, though her sons, who could cope with it all quite easily themselves, had often tried to make her give it up; but she would not hear of it, and obviously it was in this continual activity that the secret of her youthful vigour lay. She had lost her husband soon after their marriage, and I had never known him. Sometimes she would talk to me about him, but never for very long; almost at once, her voice would be choked by tears, and so I know next to nothing about my grandfather, and I was unable to picture him in my mind's eye, for neither my mother nor my uncles would talk to me about him : in our land, we hardly ever speak about dead people whom we have loved very much; we feel too sick at heart when we remember them.

Whenever I went to Tindican, it was always with my youngest uncle, who used to come to fetch me. He was younger than my mother and was not much more than an adolescent; and so I used to feel that he was still very close to my own age. He was very good-natured, and my mother did not have to tell him to look after me; he was naturally kind, and needed no telling. He would take me by the hand, and I would walk beside him; he, out of consideration for my extreme youth, would take much smaller steps, so that instead of taking two hours to reach Tindican, we would often take at least four. But I scarcely used to notice how long we were on the road, for there were all kinds of wonderful things to entertain us.

I say 'wonderful things', because Kouroussa is quite a large town and the life of the country-side and the fields is lost to us; and for a town child, such life is always wonderful. As we wandered along the road, we would startle out of their hiding-places here a hare, there a wild boar, and birds would suddenly rise up with a great rattle of wings; sometimes, too, we would encounter a band of monkeys; and always I would feel a little shock of fright in my heart, as if I myself were more startled than the wild creatures that had been warned by our

approach. Observing my rapturous delight, my uncle
would collect pebbles and throw them far in front of us,
or would beat the tall grasses with a dead branch, the
better to stir up the game. I used to imitate him, but
never for very long : in the afternoon, the sun burns
fiercely down upon the savannah; and I would soon
come back to him and slip my hand into my uncle's.
And we would wander quietly along again.

'I hope you're not feeling too tired?' my uncle would
ask.

'No.'

'We can have a little rest if you like.'

He would choose a tree — a kapok tree or any tree
that gave a sufficiency of shade — and we would sit down.
He would tell me the latest news about the farm : calv-
ings, the purchase of an ox, the clearing of land for a new
field or the misdemeanours of a wild boar; but it was
the births in particular that excited my interest.

'One of the cows has calved,' he would say.

'Which one?' I would ask, for I knew each animal
by name.

'The white one.'

'The one with horns like the crescent moon?'

'That's the one.'

'And what sort of calf is it?'

'A fine one, with a white star on his forehead.'

'A star?'

'Yes, a star.'

And for a little while I would think about that star,
I would see it in my mind's eye. A calf with a star on
his forehead : that meant he was to be the leader of the
herd.

'Oh, but he must be beautiful!' I would say.

'You can't imagine anything so beautiful. His ears
are so rosy, you'd almost think they were transparent.'

'I want to see him at once. Shall we go and see him

as soon as we arrive?'

'Of course.'

'You'll come with me, won't you?'

'I'll come with you, you little scare-cat.'

Yes, I was scared of all big animals with horns. My little playmates in Tindican used to go up to them without the slightest fear, hanging on their horns and even jumping on their backs; but I used to keep my distance. Whenever I had to go off into the bush with a drove of cattle, I would watch them grazing, but I would never go too close to them; I liked them, but I was afraid of their horns. Of course the calves had no horns, but they made sudden, unexpected movements: you couldn't really trust them.

'Come on!' I would say to my uncle. 'We've lain here long enough.'

I was impatient to get there. If the calf was in the paddock I would be able to stroke him : in the paddock, the calves were always quiet. I would put a little salt on the palm of my hand, and the calf would come and lick the salt; I would feel his tongue gently scraping my palm.

'Let's hurry!' I would cry.

But my legs weren't used to such haste, and I would soon slow down. And we would saunter along, walking as slowly as we liked. My uncle would tell me how the monkey had foiled the panther when it wanted to eat him up, or how the palm-squirrel had kept the hyena waiting all night long for nothing. These were stories I had heard a hundred times, but each time I heard them with renewed pleasure; my laughter used to send up the game all round us.

Before we even reached the outskirts of Tindican, I would see my grandmother coming to meet us. I would drop my uncle's hand and run shouting towards her. She would lift me high in the air, then press me to her bosom, and I used to squeeze her as hard as I could, flinging my arms around her, overcome with happiness.

'How are you, my little man?' she would say.

'I'm fine!' I would cry.

'Now, is that so?'

And she would look me over, feeling me; she would look and see if my cheeks were fat, and she would feel me to see if I was something more than just skin and bones. If she was satisfied in her investigations, she would congratulate me; but if her fingers felt only skin and bone – for I grew very fast, and that made me thin – she would groan.

'Just look at that!' she would say. 'Don't they give you anything to eat in town? You're not going back until you've put some flesh on these bones. D'you hear me?'

'Yes, Grandmamma.'

'And how are your mother and father and everybody at your place? Are they all well?'

And before she would set me down again, she would wait until I'd told her all the news about everyone at home.

'I hope the journey hasn't worn him out,' she would say to my uncle.

'Not at all,' he would reply. 'We've been crawling along like tortoises, and now he's ready to run like a hare.'

Then, more or less reassured, she would take my hand, and we would walk to the village, and with my hands in theirs we would all – my granny, my uncle and myself – make our entry into the village. As soon as we reached the first huts, my grandmother would shout out:

'Folks, here's my little man just arrived!'

The women would come out of their huts and run towards us, exclaiming and laughing:

'Why, he's a real little man! That's a real fine little man you've got there!'

Many of them would lift me up to press me to their bosoms. They, too, would carefully examine my appearance – how I was looking and what clothes I was wearing, for they were town clothes, and they had to declare that everything was splendid, and said that my grandmother was very lucky to have a fine little man like me. They came running from all over to greet me; as if the head of the canton in person had come to Tindican; and my grandmother would be glowing with pride and joy.

Stopped like this at every hut, acknowledging the enthusiasm of the village women and giving everyone news of my parents, it used to take at least two hours to make our way over the two hundred yards or so that divided my grandmother's hut from the first huts in the village. And when those good ladies finally did leave us, it would be to supervise the cooking of enormous plates of rice and dishes of chicken which they were to bring us for the festive dinner in the evening.

So even if I was as skinny as a rake when I arrived in Tindican, I could be certain of leaving there, ten days later, as plump as a partridge and bursting with health.

My uncle's compound was a large one. Though it contained far fewer families than our own, and though it did not have the same importance, its proportions were very generous, as things usually are in the country, where there is plenty of room. There were the paddocks for cattle and for goats; there were the granaries for rice and millet, cassava and ground-nuts, as well as for okra, which take the form of little huts raised on stone supports to protect them from the damp. With the exception of these paddocks and granaries, my uncle's compound looked very much as ours did; though its fence was stronger : instead of plaited reeds, they had used sturdy wooden posts cut in the nearby forest; as for the huts, they were built just like ours, but they were more primitive.

My Uncle Lansana, being the eldest, had inherited the compound on my grandfather's death. Actually, my uncle had a twin who might have inherited it, but Lansana had been the first-born; and among our people it is the first-born of twins who is considered the elder. However, it sometimes happens that some of the elder twin's right are transferred to the younger, for one of the twins always has a more forceful character than the other, and he becomes the heir, even though he may not be the first-born.

Maybe, in my uncles' case, it might have been the second twin who asserted his superiority, for he lacked neither skill nor authority. But such things did not interest him. He had no taste for farming and he was only rarely seen in Tindican. He led a roving existence; it was only by chance or when he made one of his infrequent visits that we knew of his whereabouts; adventure was in his blood. I myself saw him only once : he had come back to Tindican; he was only there a few days but all the time he thought only of getting away again. I remember him as an extremely attractive character who talked a great deal; in fact he never stopped talking, and I could have listened to him for hours on end. He would talk about his adventures, which were curious and disturbing and opened up astonishing vistas to me. He used to load me up with presents. Was he putting himself out to please the schoolboy I then was, or was it simply that he was by nature generous? I do not know. When I saw him setting out for fresh adventures, I wept. What was he called? I cannot remember; maybe I never knew. During the few days he remained at Tindican, I called him Bo, and that was what I called my Uncle Lansana also, for that is the name usually given to twins, and this nickname often takes the place of their real one.

My Uncle Lansana had two other brothers, one of whom had recently married; the younger, the one who had come to fetch me from Kouroussa, was engaged, though he was still too young to take a wife. So that there were two families, though they were not very large, dwelling in the compound besides my grandmother and my youngest uncle.

Generally, on my arrival in the afternoon, my Uncle Lansana would still be at work in the fields, and I would go straight to my grandmother's hut, the one I was to stay in throughout my visit.

The inside of this hut closely resembled the one I shared with my mother at Kouroussa; there was even the same sort of calabash as the one my mother had for keeping the milk in, suspended just in the same way by three ropes from the roof so that none of the animals could reach it, and covered with the same sort of lid to prevent the soot from falling in it. The thing that made this hut different, as far as I was concerned, was that there were ears of maize hanging from the roof-top in countless garlands which grew smaller and smaller as they approached the summit; the smoke from the fire kept circling among the ears and so preserved them from attack by termites and mosquitoes. These garlands might have served as a rustic calendar, for as the harvest-time came round again, their number would decrease, until finally there would be none left.

But for the moment I would go into the hut only in order to take my clothes off : my grandmother felt that after walking from Kouroussa, the first thing to do was to give myself a bath. She wanted me at least to start my visit clean, though she had no illusions about how long such cleanliness would last; so she would take me straight away to the wash-place, a small enclosure near the hut, surrounded by a reed fence and paved with large stones. Then she would go back to the hut, take the pot from the fire, and pour the hot water into a calabash. After she had cooled it to the right temperature, she would carry it into the wash-place. There she would soap me from head to foot with black soap, then rub me roughly down with a sponge made of tow from the dried stems of pulpy plants. I would leave the hut, all shining with wet, my blood racing under my gleaming skin, my hair black as pitch, and run to dry myself in front of the fire.

My little playmates would be waiting there for me.

'So you've come back?' they would say.

'I've come back.'

'For how long?'

'For a little while.'

Then, according to whether I was thin or plump – for to them too, how one looked was of the first importance, and I was usually thin as a rake – I would hear:

'My! *you're* looking well!'

'Oh!' I would modestly reply.

Or:

'You've not got much flesh on you!'

'I'm growing up,' would be my dignified reply. 'When you're growing up, you don't have much flesh on your bones.'

'Y-yes . . . all the same, you're too thin.'

And they would fall silent for a while as they each turned over in their minds this strange growth which makes city children thinner than country children. Then one of them would invariably shout:

'You've never seen as many birds as there are in the fields this year!'

But each year it was the same: there were always great flocks of birds laying waste the crops, and we, the children, always had the job of driving them away.

'I've got my sling,' I would say.

I had brought it with me : I would never have dreamt of leaving it behind, and here I carried it with me all the time, whether I was watching the cattle grazing or guarding the crops from the top of the look-out posts.

These posts used to play an important part in my visit to Tindican : everywhere there were to be seen these platforms mounted on forked stakes that looked as if they were riding the great flowing seas of the harvest fields. With my little playmates I would climb the ladder to one of them and scare the birds, and sometimes the monkeys that came to raid our fields. At any rate, that is what we were supposed to do, and we did it without grumbling, for it was more of a pleasure than a duty. But it sometimes happened that we became absorbed in other games, and forgot why we were there. And though I did not suffer for this forgetfulness, my playmates often did : their parents were not slow to discover that the crops had not been properly watched, and then, depending on how much damage had been done, the careless watchers had their vigilance improved by a sharp scolding or by the whip. Nevertheless, though suitably chastened, we chattered all the time, exchanging those exciting little secrets that are not for grown-up ears, and which were mostly accounts of childish little thefts, while still keeping an eye on the crops; in any case, our shouts and our singing were generally sufficient to keep the birds away, even the millet-eaters that used to descend in dense flocks on the fields.

My little playmates were very kind to me. They were really wonderful friends, daring – certainly more daring than I was – and even a little reckless : but they would moderate their natural impetuosity out of consideration for the town child I was, and they held in great respect this little city-dweller who used to come and join in their rural games; they were always filled with admiration for my schoolboy clothes.

As soon as I had got dry in front of the fire, I would put them on again. My little playmates would watch me with envious eyes as I slipped on my short-sleeved khaki shirt, my shorts of the same colour, and my sandals. I also had a beret, which I hardly ever wore. But these small splendours were enough to dazzle the eyes of the country children, whose only covering was a brief loin-cloth. For my part, I envied them their loin-cloth, which allowed them much more liberty of movement. Those town clothes, which had to be kept clean, were a real nuisance : they got dirty, and were easily torn. When we were climbing up the observation-posts, I had to take great care not to catch my trousers on the rough wooden rungs; when we were on the platform at the top, I had to keep away from the fresh-cut sheaves of corn, which were put there to be used for next season's sowing, out of the reach of termites. And if we lit a fire to roast the lizards or the field-mice which we killed with our slings, I did not dare approach too close, or attempt to skin the spoils of the hunt : the blood would have marked my clothes, and the fire would have blackened them; I had to stand by and watch the lizards or the field-mice being cleaned, and their insides filled with salt before they were placed on the fire; and even while I was eating them, all kinds of precautions were necessary.

So I would gladly have given up those schoolboy garments which were only suitable for town wear; and, in fact, I would very soon have discarded them if I had had anything else to put on, but those were the only clothes I had with me, and no others were given me; here at any rate I could dirty them or tear them without being scolded : my grandmother used to wash them and mend them without any fuss. I had come to run and play and climb up the look-out posts and wander off into the long grass with the flocks and herds, and naturally

I could not do these things without some damage to my precious clothes.

At nightfall, my Uncle Lansana would come back from the fields. He would greet me after his own quiet fashion, for he was rather timid and spoke little. Working alone in the fields all day, you get used to being silent; you think of all kinds of things, and then you start all over again, because thoughts are something you can never grasp completely : the mute mystery of things, their how and why predisposes you to silence. It is enough to call such things to mind and to become aware of their inscrutable mystery which leaves behind it a certain light in the eyes. My Uncle Lansana's eyes were singularly piercing when he looked at you; actually, he very rarely looked at you : he would remain usually rapt in that inner dream which obsessed him endlessly in the fields.

When we were all together at meal-times I would often turn my eyes towards my uncle, and generally, after a moment or two, I would succeed in catching his eye. There was always a smile behind the gravity of his gaze, for my uncle was goodness itself and he loved me; I really believe he loved me as much as my grandmother did. I would respond to his gently smiling glance, and sometimes, as I always ate very slowly, it would make me forget to eat.

'You're not eating anything,' my grandmother would say.

'Yes, I am eating,' I would reply.

'That's right,' my grandmother would say, 'you must eat it all up !'

But of course it was impossible to eat up all the meat and rice that had been prepared to celebrate my happy arrival; my little friends used to lend an eager hand with it, too. They had all been invited, and used to go for the food with the frank appetites of young wolves;

but there was too much, there was always too much: we could never get to the end of such a meal.

'Look how round my belly is!' I would hear myself saying.

Yes, our little bellies *were* round, and sitting afterwards round the fire, solemnly digesting our food, we might easily have fallen asleep if we had not had such naturally lively dispositions. But we had our palavers to hold, like our elders; we had not seen each other for weeks, sometimes months, and we had so many things to tell each other, so many new stories to relate, and this was the time for them!

Of course we all had our own stories to tell, we knew lots of them, but there would always be some stories that we were hearing for the first time, and those were the ones we were most eager to listen to as we sat round the fire, and it was the tellers of these tales who would get the most applause.

In this fashion my first day in the country would come to a close, unless someone brought out a tom-tom, for this was a special occasion. And in Tindican it was not every evening you heard the tom-tom.

Four

DECEMBER ALWAYS found me at Tindican. December is our dry season, when we have fine weather and harvest our rice. Year after year I was invited to this harvest, which is always the occasion of great junketings and feastings, and I used to wait impatiently for my uncle to come and fetch me.

Of course, the festival had no set date, since it depended on the ripening of the rice, and this, in turn, depended on the weather, the goodwill of the heavens. It depended perhaps still more on the goodwill of the spirits of the soil, whose influence could not be ignored. If their response was favourable, it only remained to beg of them, on the day before the harvest, to provide sunny skies and protection for the harvesters against the danger of snake-bites.

When the great day had arrived, the head of each family would rise at dawn to go and cut the first swathe in his fields. As soon as this first sheaf had been cut, the tom-tom would sound, signalling the beginning of the harvest. Such is our custom. I could not have said then why this was done : why the signal was given only after the first swathe had been cut in each of the fields. I only know that such was the custom, and that was enough for me. Like all our customs, this one must have had its own significance, which I could have easily found out from the elders of the village, who kept its secret meaning in the ancestral depths of heart and memory. But at that time I was not old enough or curious enough to ask my elders and betters, and when finally I wanted to do so, I had left Africa behind.

Today I am inclined to think that these first swathes were cut in order to break the spell of inviolability which one feels at the sight of an unmown field; but I do not remember that these swathes served any particular purpose once they had been cut : I do not remember them being used as offerings. Sometimes only the spirit of a tradition survives, and so it happens that the merest ghost of an outward ceremony remains. Was that the case here? I cannot say; though I made frequent visits to Tindican, they did not last long enough for me to find out everything. All I know is that the tom-tom used to sound only after the first sheaf had been gathered, and that we used to await the signal eagerly, because we were always in a hurry to get to work, and also because we wanted to leave the rather chilly shadow of the great trees at the edge of the fields, where the morning air used to be piercingly cold.

When the signal had been given, the reapers used to set out, and I would fall into step with them, marching to the rhythm of the tom-tom. The young men used to toss their glittering sickles high in the air and catch them as they fell, shouting aloud for the simple pleasure of hearing their own strong young voices, and sketching a dance step or two on the heels of the tom-tom players. I suppose I should have done well to follow my grandmother's advice and to keep at a safe distance from those lively jugglers. But there was such a vivid freshness in the morning air, such scintillating vivacity in their juggling feats, in the spinning sickles that in the rising sun would blaze and flash with sudden brilliance, and there was such irresistible alacrity in the rhythm of the tom-tom that I could never have kept myself away from them.

Besides, at that particular season it was impossible not to want to join in everything. In our December, the whole world is in flower and the air is sweet : everything is young and fresh; the spring seems linked with the summer, and the country-side that for so long has been drenched in rain and shrouded in baleful mists now lies radiant; the sky has never seemed so blue, so brilliant; the birds are ecstatically singing; there is joy all round us – its gentle explosions are echoed in every heart. It was this season, this beautiful time of every year, that was stirring me so deeply, and the beat of the tom-tom and the festive air of our little procession moved me also. It was the best time of the year, the summer and all it stands for, all it holds and cannot hold – for how could it contain so much profusion? – and it made my heart leap with joy.

When they had arrived at the first harvest-field, the

men would line up at the edge, naked to the loins, their sickles at the ready. Then my Uncle Lansana or some other farmer – for the harvest threw people together and everyone lent a hand in each other's harvesting – would invite them to begin work. At once the black torsos would bend over the great golden field, and the sickles would begin the reaping. Now it was not only the breeze of morning that was making the whole field sway and shiver, but the men also, with their sickles.

These sickles kept rising and falling with astonishing rapidity and regularity. They had to cut the stalk between the bottom joint and the lowest leaf, so that only the leaf was left behind; well, they hardly ever missed. Of course, such a degree of accuracy depended on the reaper: he would hold the ear with one hand and incline the stalk to receive a clean blow from the sickle. He would reap the ears one by one, but the swift rise and fall of the sickle was nevertheless amazing. Besides, each man made it a point of honour to reap as accurately and as swiftly as possible; he would move forward across the field with a bunch of stalks in his hand, and his fellow-workmen would judge his skill by the number and the size of his sheaves.

My young uncle was wonderfully skilful at rice-cutting: in fact there was no one to touch him at it. I would follow proudly behind him, ready to take each sheaf as he cut it. When I had taken a sheaf from him, I would strip the stalks of their leaves then trim them all to an equal length and pile them up. And I would always take care to do this very gently, for rice is harvested only when it is very ripe, and if it is roughly handled the ears lose the best part of their grains. I did not tie the sheaves, for that was a man's job, but once they had been tied, I was allowed to go and put them on the great pile in the centre of the field.

As the morning drew on, it would become hotter, the

air seeming to quiver in a dense heat-haze which was intensified by clouds of dust from the trampled soil and stubble. This was the moment when my uncle would wipe the sweat from his forehead and his chest and ask for his water-bottle. I would run and fetch it from under the leaves where it lay, fresh and cool, and offer it to him with the words :

'Will you leave some for me ?'

'You don't think I would drink it all, do you ?'

But I would watch anxiously as, holding the flask high in the air, he quaffed great draughts of the water without touching the flask to his lips.

'There, that's better,' he would say, handing the bottle to me. 'The dust cakes in your throat.'

I would put my lips to the bottle, and at once the coolness of the water would make itself felt throughout my whole body with a kind of fresh interior radiance. But its refreshment was only momentary : it was soon forgotten, and left my body bathed in sweat.

'Take your shirt off,' my uncle would say. 'It's soaking wet. You shouldn't keep wet things on your chest.'

And he would start work again, and I would start following him again, proud to see that we were the leaders.

'Aren't you tired ?' I would ask him.

'Why should I be tired ?'

'Your sickle moves so quickly.'

'It does, doesn't it ?'

'We're ahead of all the others.'

'Oh ? Are we ?'

'You know we are !' I would cry. 'Why do you say "Oh, are we ?" like that ?'

'I don't want to boast, you know.'

'No, of course not.'

And I would begin to wonder if I should ever be able

to do what he was doing one day, and to do it as well
as he did.

'Won't you let me reap for a while?'

'What would your grandmother say? A sickle is
not a plaything: you have no idea how sharp it is!'

'Yes, I do.'

'Now it isn't your job to cut rice. I shouldn't think
it ever will be: later on . . .'

But I didn't like to be so easily put off from working
in the fields. 'Later . . .' Why only 'later' . . .? I did not
see why I should not become a reaper like the rest of
them, a farmer too. Was it because . . .

'Well, are you dreaming?' my uncle would say.

And I would take the bundle of stalks he handed me,
strip off the leaves and trim the stalks. Yes, I had been
day-dreaming: my life did not lie here . . . nor in my
father's forge, either. Then what sort of life was I going
to lead? And I would tremble at the thought of the
unknown existence ahead of me. Wouldn't it have been
simpler to follow in my father's footsteps? 'School . . .
school . . .' I would say to myself. Did I like school all
that much? Maybe I did. My uncles . . . Yes, my uncles
had followed quite naturally in their father's footsteps,
though others had taken a different course: my father's
brothers had gone to Conakry; my Uncle Lansana's
twin brother was . . . But where *was* he now?

'Well, still day-dreaming?' my uncle would ask.

'Yes . . . No . . . I . . .'

'If you go on like this, we'll lose the lead.'

'I was thinking about Uncle Bo. Where is he now?'

'God only knows! On his last visit, he was . . . You
see, I don't know where he is any more! He's never
in the same place: he's like a bird: he can't stay quietly
on one tree, he needs the whole sky.'

'Will I, too, be like a bird some day?'

'What *are* you talking about?'

'Well, you've just told me that Uncle Bo is like a bird.'

'Do you want to become like him?'

'I don't know yet.'

'Well, you have plenty of time to make your mind up, anyhow. Meanwhile, take this sheaf.'

And he would go on reaping. Even though his body was soaking wet, he always returned to his work with great vigour, as if he were only just beginning. But all the same, the heat was a burden; the air would seem to weigh down upon us; and weariness would gradually begin to creep over us : draughts of cold water were no longer any good, and so we would begin to fight our weariness with singing.

'Sing with us,' my uncle would say.

The tom-tom, which had been following us as we advanced into the field, kept time with our singing. We sang like a choir, often very high, with great bursts of melody, and sometimes very low, so low that we could hardly be heard. And our weariness would disappear, the heat grow less.

If, on such occasions, I paused for a moment and gazed at the reapers, the long, sinuous line of reapers, I would always be struck, delightfully touched, enraptured in fact, by the tenderness, the vast, infinite tenderness in their eyes, by the immense serenity of their gaze — and that does not mean it was remote or preoccupied — as they looked about them from time to time. And yet, although they all seemed to me at such moments 'miles away' from what they were doing, though their eyes seemed far away from what they were doing, their skill never faltered; the dark hands and the glittering sickles kept moving with an unbroken, almost abstracted precision.

What was it those eyes were actually gazing at? I do not know. The surrounding country-side? Maybe.

Maybe it was the distant trees, and the far-off sky. Maybe not. Maybe those eyes were gazing at nothing, fixed on the invisible, and maybe that is what made them appear so tranced, so abstracted. The long wavering line of reapers kept on moving deeper and deeper into the field, laying it bare; wasn't that enough? Wasn't it enough to see the ears of rice bowing before the long, gentle wave of those black bodies? Our husbandmen were singing, and as they sang, they reaped; they were singing in chorus, and reaping in unison : their voices and their gestures were all harmonious, and in harmony; they were one – united by the same task, united by the same song. They were bound to one another, united by the same soul : each and every one was tasting the delight, savouring the common pleasure of accomplishing a common task.

Was it this delight, this pleasure, even more than the fight against weariness and against the burden of the heat, that urged them on, that filled them to overflowing with rapturous song? Such was obviously the case : and this is what filled their eyes with so much tenderness, that wonderful serenity that used to strike me with such delighted and rather regretful astonishment; for though I was among them, with them, surrounded by these waves of tenderness, I was not one of them : I was only a schoolboy on a visit – and how I longed to forget that fact!

Actually, I often *did* forget it; I was still very young and was often able to forget myself in the moment; everything that passed through my head – and that was a great deal – was almost always fleeting and less enduring than the clouds that moved across the summer sky; and besides, I was at the age – I shall never grow out of it! – when one lives entirely in the present; and in those days, holding the first position in the long line of reapers seemed to have more importance than anything I would be likely to do in the future.

'Make haste!' I would urge my uncle.

'Oh! So you've woken up at last?' he would tease me.

'Yes. We mustn't waste any more time.'

'Who's been wasting time? Me?'

'No, but you might if we go on like this: we're not so far ahead now.'

'Oh?'

And he would take a look round the field.

'Is that what you call not being so far ahead? Well, I'm pretty sure I've not been wasting my time, but maybe I ought to now. Don't forget I mustn't get too far ahead of the others: it would not be polite.'

I do not know how the idea of 'rustic' manners – I use the word in its accepted sense of 'lacking in delicacy' – came to be associated with the people of the fields. The outward forms of common civility are more scrupulously observed in the country than in the town; there a certain ceremony in manners is observed which the town has no time for. The way of life, of course, is simpler in the country, but a countryman's dealings with his fellow-men follow accepted rules. Familiarity is discouraged, perhaps *because* country people are familiar with every detail of each other's lives. In everything I noticed a kind of dignity which was often lacking in town life; no one ever did anything without first having been ceremoniously invited to do so, even though he had a right to do so. The personal liberty of others was in fact always highly respected. And if their minds seemed to work slower in the country that was because they always spoke only after due reflection, and because speech itself was a most serious matter.

At midday, the women, bearing steaming platters of *couscous,* would leave the huts and walk single file to the field. As soon as we caught sight of them, we would shout our greetings. Midday! It was midday! And work would stop all over the field.

'Come on,' my uncle would say.

And I would run along behind him.

'Not so fast!' I would say. 'I can't keep up with you.'

'Is there a hole in your stomach?' he would ask me. 'I could stable an ox in mine, I'm so hungry!'

And our appetites were in fact wonderfully whetted. However strong the sun, however furnace-hot the field with its dust and its quivering haze, it did not interfere with our appetites. We would squat down round the platters, and the hot *couscous,* made even hotter by the spices in it, would disappear, engulfed in great hungry mouthfuls, washed down by bumpers of cool water drawn from huge jars covered with banana leaves.

The break would last until two o'clock, and the men would spend the time sleeping in the shade of the trees or sharpening their sickles. Tireless, the young lads would play games or go and set snares; and though we would as usual make a lot of noise, we would take care not to whistle, because we were not supposed to whistle or pick up dead wood during the time of the harvest: such things would have brought misfortune to the fields.

The afternoon's work was much shorter and the time used to fly. It would be five o'clock before we knew it. The great field would now be shorn of its precious yield, and we would walk back in procession to the village – the tall silk-cotton trees and the wavering smoke from the huts seemed to welcome us from far off – preceded by the indefatigable tom-tom player, and singing at the tops of our voices the Song of the Rice.

Overhead, the swallows would already be skimming lower, though the air would still be clear as ever; but they, too, knew when the end of the day was near. We would go home contented, weary but happy. The good spirits had taken care of us: not one of us had been bitten by snakes that our trampling feet might have disturbed. The flowers, which would begin to unfold with the approach of evening, would be spreading their perfume on the air again, so that we walked as if attired in freshly-plucked garlands. If we had not been singing so loudly, we might have been able to hear the familiar sounds of the close of day: the shouts and laughter of women mingling with the lowing of cattle returning to their byres. But we were singing, always singing! Ah! How happy we were in those days!

Five

At Kouroussa, I lived in my mother's hut. My brothers, who were younger, and my sisters, the eldest of whom came twelve months after me, all used to sleep in my father's mother's hut. I did not have the hut's second bed to myself. This was because the huts were so small. But I shared this bed with my father's youngest apprentices.

My father always had a lot of apprentices in his workshop; they came from far and near, often from very remote districts, mainly, I think, because he treated them so well, but above all because his skill as a craftsman was widely acknowledged; and also, I imagine, because there was always plenty of work at his forge. But these apprentices had to have somewhere to sleep.

Those who had reached manhood had their own hut. The youngest, those who, like me, were still uncircumcised, slept in my mother's hut. My father certainly thought they could have no better lodging. My mother was very kind, very correct. She also had great authority, and kept an eye on everything we did; so that her kindness was not altogether untempered by severity. But how could it have been otherwise, when there were at that time, apart from the apprentices, a dozen or so children running about the compound, children who were not good all the time, but always so full of life that they must often have sorely tried their mother's patience – and my mother was not a very patient woman.

I see now that she was more patient with the apprentices than she was with her own children. She put herself out for them more than she did for us. The apprentices were far from home, and both my mother and my father were very affectionate with them, coddling them like babies, and indulging them more than they did their own children. I was certainly my mother's chief concern, though she did not show it. The apprentices were encouraged to think of themselves as on an equal footing with the master's children. I thought of them all as elder brothers.

I remember one of them in particular: Sidafa. He was a little older than myself, very lively, thin but vigorous, hot-blooded, always full of projects and ideas of every kind. As my days were spent at school, and his in the workshop, the only time we had for chattering was when we went to bed. The air in the hut was warm, and the oil-lamps at the side of the bed cast a dim light. I would repeat to Sidafa what I had been learning in school that day: and he for his part would recount in detail all that had gone on in the workshop. My mother, whose bed was separated from ours only by the width of the hearth, had of necessity to listen to our chatter. At least she would listen for a while: she would soon get weary of it.

'Have you two gone to bed to chatter or to sleep?' she would say. 'Now go to sleep, both of you!'

'Just a little longer, please, I haven't finished my story,' I would plead.

Or I would get up and take a drink of water to the canary who, perched over his little bed of gravel, had lost his voice. But the respite I asked for was not always granted; though when it was, we used to abuse the privilege, so that my mother would sooner or later interrupt us sharply.

'Now that's enough of that!' she would say. 'I don't want to hear another word. You'll neither of you be able to get up in the morning.'

Which was true: if we were never in any great hurry to go to sleep, neither were we ever in any great hurry to get up. So we would stop our chattering. The beds were not far enough removed from my mother's sharp ears for us to be able to converse in whispers. But as soon as we were quiet, we very quickly used to feel our eyes grow heavy; the cosy crackling of the fire and the warmth of the bedclothes did the rest: we would gradually drift off into sleep.

In the morning, when, after some persuasion, we rose, we would find the breakfast all ready. My mother used to get up at dawn to prepare it. We all would squat round the great steaming platters: my parents, sisters, brothers, and the apprentices, those who shared my bed as well as those who had their own hut. There would be one dish for the men, and another for my mother and my sisters.

It would not be exactly right for me to say that my mother presided over the meal: my father was the one who did that. Nevertheless, it was my mother's presence that made itself felt first of all. Was that because she had prepared the food, because meals are mainly a woman's business? Maybe. But there was something else: my mother, by the mere fact of her presence, and even though she was not seated immediately in front of the men's dish, saw to it that everything was done according to her own set of rules: and those rules were strict.

For example, it was forbidden to cast my gaze upon guests older than myself, and I was also forbidden to talk: my whole attention had to be fixed on the food in front of me. In fact, it would have been considered most impolite to chatter at that moment. Even my younger brothers knew that this was no time to jabber: this was the moment to honour our food. Older people observed more or less the same silence. This was not the only rule: those concerning cleanliness were no less important. Finally, if there was meat on the dish, I was not allowed to help myself from the centre, but only from the part directly in front of me: my father would put more within my reach if he saw that I needed it. Any other behaviour would have been frowned upon and quickly reprimanded. In any case, my own portion was always so generous that I should never have been tempted to take more than I was given.

When the meal was over, I would say, 'Thank you, Father.'

The apprentices would all say, 'Thank you, Master.'

Then I would bow to my mother and say, 'The meal was good, Mother.'

My brothers, my sisters and the apprentices would do likewise. Then my parents would reply, 'Thank you,' to each one of them. Such was the rule. My father would certainly have been offended to see it broken, but it was my mother, with her quick temper, who rebuked any transgression. My father's mind was already on his work, and he left these prerogatives to her.

I realise that my mother's authoritarian attitudes may appear surprising; generally the role of the African woman is thought to be a ridiculously humble one, and indeed there are parts of the continent where it *is* insignificant; but Africa is vast, with a correspondingly vast diversity of types. In our country, the woman's role is one of fundamental independence; she has great personal pride. We despise only those who allow themselves to be despised; and our women very seldom give cause for that. My father would never have dreamed of despising anyone, least of all my mother. He had the greatest respect for her, and so did our friends and neighbours. That was due, I am sure, to my mother's character, which was impressive; it was due also to the strange powers she possessed.

I hesitate to say what these powers were, and I do not wish to describe them all. I know that what I have to tell you will perhaps be greeted with sceptical smiles. And today, now that I come to think about them, even I hardly know what to make of them. They seem to me incredible; they *are* incredible. Nevertheless, I can only tell you what I saw with my own eyes. How could I disown the testimony of my own eyes? I saw those incredible things. I seem to see them again as I saw them then. Are there not things everywhere around us that are incapable of explanation? In our country there were mysteries without number, and my mother was familiar with all of them.

One day – it was towards evening – I saw some men come and request her to use her powers to get a horse on his feet after he had resisted all attempts to make him rise. He was out at pasture, but he was lying down and his owner wanted to bring him back to the stable before nightfall. The horse obstinately refused to move, although there was no apparent reason why he should disobey. But his inclination was otherwise, and it may have been some magic spell that was keeping him from moving. I heard the men telling my mother about it, and asking her help.

'Let's go and have a look at this horse, then,' said my mother.

She called the eldest of my sisters and told her to look after the cooking of the evening meal, and then went off with the men. I followed after her. When we arrived at the pasture, we saw the horse: he was lying on the grass, gazing at us unconcernedly. His owner tried again to make him get up and spoke to him in honeyed tones, but the horse remained deaf to all entreaty. His master raised a hand to strike him.

'Do not strike him,' said my mother. 'It won't do any good.'

She went up to the horse and, lifting her hand, declaimed in a solemn tone of voice: 'If it be true that from the day of my birth I had knowledge of no man until the day of my marriage: and if it be true that from the day of my marriage I have had knowledge of no man other than my lawful husband – if these things be true, then I command you, horse, rise up!'

And we all saw the horse get up at once and follow his master quietly away. I have told in very simple language, but very precisely, what I saw that day, saw with my own eyes; and to my mind the thing is incredible: but the event was just as I have described it: the horse got up without any further delay and followed his master. If he had refused to follow him, my mother would have intervened once more, until she had achieved the desired effect.

Where did these powers come from? Well, my mother was born immediately after my twin uncles in Tindican. Now they say that twin brothers are wiser than other children, and are practically magicians: for the child that follows them, and who receives the name 'sayon', that is, the younger brother of twins, he, too, is endowed with the gift of magic, and he is even considered to be more powerful than the twins, in whose lives he plays a very important role, because his birth is even more mysterious than theirs. So if it happens that twins fall out, it is to the 'sayon's' authority that they appeal to settle the matter; indeed, he is accredited with a wisdom greater than that of the twins, and is given more consideration : it goes without saying that his interventions are always conducted, must be conducted, in the most tactful way.

It is the custom with us for twins to agree about everything, and they have by right a more precise equality of treatment than is accorded to other children : if something is given to one, the other must be given the same thing also. It is an obligation which must never be disregarded; if it is, the twins are both equally hurt, settle the matter between themselves, and in certain cases cast a spell upon the person who has injured them. If any kind of dispute should arise between them – if one, for example, has a plan which the other thinks is foolish – they make an appeal to their younger brother and are happy to accept his decision.

I have given one example of my mother's supernatural powers; I could give many others, equally strange, equally mysterious. How many times have I not seen my mother, at daybreak, walking a few steps into the yard and turning her head in one direction or another to shout at the top of her voice :

'If this business goes any further, I shall not hesitate to expose you. That's my final word!'

Her voice, in the early morning, travelled far : it was intended to reach the ears of the witch-doctor, for whom the warning had been uttered. He understood that if he did not stop his nocturnal activities, my mother would denounce him in public; and this threat always worked : from then on the witch-doctor would remain quiet. My mother used to receive warning of these activities while she was asleep; that is why we never wakened her, for fear of interrupting the course of the revelations that flowed through her dreams. This power was well known by our neighbours and by the whole community : no one ever doubted it.

As well as this gift, or rather part-gift, of magic, my mother had other powers that she had inherited in the same way. Her father, at Tindican, had been a skilful blacksmith, and my mother possessed the usual powers of that caste, from which the majority of circumcisers and many soothsayers are drawn. My mother's brothers had chosen to be farmers, but if they had not followed their father's trade that was their own affair. Perhaps my Uncle Lansana, the silent one, who was a great dreamer, in fixing his choice upon a farm-worker's life, upon the immense peace of the fields, had led his brothers away from the paternal forge. Was he, also, a soothsayer? I am inclined to think he was. He had the customary powers of a twin, and the powers of his caste; only I do not think he showed them very often. It was in my mother that the spirit of her caste was most visibly – I was going to say ostensibly – manifested. Finally, she had naturally inherited from my grandfather his totem, which is the crocodile. This totem allowed all Damans to draw water from the Niger with impunity.

Normally everyone draws their water from the river. The Niger flows slowly and abundantly; it can be forded; and the crocodiles, that keep to the deep water upstream or downstream from where the water is drawn, are not to be feared. You can bathe quite freely on the banks of pale sand, and do your washing there.

But at the time of the rising of the waters, the volume of the river is increased threefold; everywhere there is deep water and the crocodiles are dangerous. You can see their triangular heads breaking the surface of the water. So everyone keeps away from the river and draws his water from the little streams.

But my mother used to continue to draw water from the river. I would watch her draw water from the part where there were crocodiles. Naturally, I used to watch her from a distance, for my totem is not my mother's, and I had every reason to fear those voracious beasts; but my mother could draw water without fear, and no one warned her of the danger, because everyone knew that the danger did not exist for her. Whoever had ventured to do what my mother used to do would inevitably have been knocked down by a blow from a powerful tail, seized in the terrible jaws and dragged into deep water. But the crocodiles could do no harm to my mother; and this privilege is quite understandable : the totem is identified with its possessor : this identification is absolute, and of such a nature that its possessor has the power to take on the form of the totem itself; it follows quite obviously that the totem cannot devour itself. My uncles at Tindican enjoyed the same prerogative.

I do not wish to say more and I have told you only what I saw with my own eyes. These miracles — they were miracles indeed — nowadays I think about them as if they were the fabulous events of a far-off past. That past is, however, still quite near : it was only yesterday. But the world rolls on, the world changes, my own world perhaps more rapidly than anyone's; so that it appears as if we are ceasing to be what we were, and that truly we are no longer what we were, and that we were not exactly ourselves even at the time when these miracles took place before our eyes. Yes, the world rolls on, and changes. I, too, had my totem, but I no longer remember what it was.

Six

I STARTED school very early. I began by attending the Moslem school, and a little later I was enrolled in the French school. Neither my mother nor I had any notion how long I would be a student at the latter: had she guessed the number of years I should be there, I am sure she would have kept me at home. But perhaps my father had guessed already . . .

Immediately after breakfast my sister and I would start out for school, carrying our exercise-books and note-books in a satchel made of raffia.

On the way we would be joined by school-mates, and the nearer we got to the school buildings the larger our little band would grow. My sister would keep with the girls, and I would walk with the boys. And like all little boys we liked to tease the girls and pull their hair; and the girls gave as good as they got, and used to laugh in our faces. But if we pulled their hair, their reprisals did not stop at calling us names: they would fight back with teeth and nails for all they were worth, scratching and kicking and biting as hard as ever they could, though this did not noticeably diminish our fondness for them. The only one I did not touch was my sister, and in return she did not interfere with my activities either. Fanta, one of her friends, also let me alone, though I can't say I did the same to her.

'Why did you pull my hair?' she asked me one day when we were alone in the school yard.

'Why shouldn't I pull it? You're a girl!'

'But I've never done anything to you!'

'No, that's true,' I said.

And for a moment I stopped to think. Until that moment, I had not realised that she was the only girl, apart from my sister, who had never hit me.

'Why didn't you hit me?' I said.

'Because!'

'Because? What sort of an answer's that?'

'Even if you were to pull my hair this minute, I would not hit you.'

'All right then, I'm going to pull your hair!'

But what would have been the point of pulling her hair? Boys did that sort of thing only when they were all together. And because I did not carry out my threat she burst out laughing.

'Just you wait till we're going home!' I said. 'It won't do you any harm to wait!'

She laughed and ran away. But when we were going home, again something prevented me from pulling her hair, and from then on I rarely bothered her. My sister was not long in noticing this.

'You don't pull Fanta's hair any more,' she said.

'Why should I pull her hair?' I answered. 'She doesn't hurt me.'

'Do you think I haven't noticed?'

'Then you know why I don't pull her hair.'

'Really?' she asked. 'Is that the only reason?'

What was she getting at? I shrugged my shoulders. It was a lot of little-girl nonsense: they did not know what they were talking about most of the time. All girls were like that.

'Shut up talking about Fanta!' I said. 'You make me tired.'

But she only began shrieking with laughter.

'Listen here,' I said, 'if you don't stop laughing at me . . .'

She made sure she was well out of my reach, then suddenly started to shout:

'Fanta! ... Fanta! ...'

'Will you shut up?' I said.

But she just went on louder than ever, and I rushed at her, but she ran away shouting:

'Fanta! ... Fanta! ...'

I looked all round me to see if I couldn't find a stone to throw at her; but there weren't any. 'I'll pay you back for that,' I said to myself.

Once in school, we went straight to our seats, boys and girls sitting side by side, our quarrels over; and, as soon as we sat down, we became all ears, and sat absolutely still, so that the teacher used to give his lessons in an impressive silence. I should just like to have seen what would have happened if we had so much as stirred in our seats. Our teacher moved like quicksilver: he never remained long in the same place; he was here, there and everywhere. His flow of talk would have bewildered less attentive pupils. But we were remarkably attentive, and we found it no strain to be so. Young though we were, we all regarded our school work as something deadly serious. Everything we learned was strange and unexpected; it was as if we were learning about life on another planet; and we never grew tired of listening. Even if it had been otherwise, the silence could not have been more absolute under the strict discipline of a master who seemed to be everywhere at once and who would never have given us an opportunity to let our attention wander or to interrupt. But as I have said, an interruption was out of the question: it simply did not occur to us. And so we tried to attract the teacher's attention as little as possible: for we lived in constant dread of being sent out to the blackboard.

This blackboard was our nightmare. Its dark, blank mirror was the exact reflection of the amount of our knowledge. We knew very little, and the little we knew was very shaky: the slightest thing could upset it. Now if we did not want to be the recipients of several strokes of the cane, we had to go to the blackboard and take the chalk in our hands and pay our debt in kind. Here the tiniest detail was of the utmost importance: the wretched blackboard magnified every mistake. If we made one of the downward strokes not exactly of the same height as the others, we were required either to do an extra lesson on Sunday, or we had to go to the teacher during break, and receive, in the class that was always known as the infants', an unforgettable beating on our bare backsides. Irregular downward strokes used to horrify our teacher: he would examine our exercise-books under a magnifying-glass, and for each irregularity he discovered we got a stroke. I remember him well, a man like quicksilver; and he wielded his stick with joyous abandon!

This was how things were in the lower classes. In the upper school, there were not so many beatings, but other kinds of punishment, hardly more pleasant, took their place. Indeed, I experienced a great variety of punishments at that school: only my own discomfort lacked variety. Our love of knowledge had to be ineradicable to survive such ordeals.

The easiest form of punishment, for second-year pupils, was sweeping the school yard. Not until then did we realise how vast it was, nor how many guava trees were planted in it. We could have sworn that the guava trees had been put there simply to litter the ground with their leaves, for we certainly never were allowed to taste any of the fruit. In the third and fourth years our punishment was to work in the kitchen-garden; it has since struck me that no cheaper form of labour could have been found. In our last two years, however, while we were studying for our proficiency certificate, the school authorities had such confidence in us – a confidence that we would gladly have done without – that we were entrusted with the herd of cattle which belonged to the school.

This task was no sinecure! You wouldn't have found a less easily managed herd for miles around. If a farmer had a vicious cow, it would be sure to end up in our herd. There was good reason for this: the farmer obviously would only be too anxious to get rid of his awkward beast, and naturally had to sell it at a loss. The school authorities were only too glad to make a profit, and did so. But it was pure stinginess. And so our school owned the most peculiar, the most heterogeneous and the most complete collection of bad-tempered old beasts in existence. If we shouted to them to go to the right, they would of course go to the left.

These beasts used to gallop madly about the bush, as they were constantly plagued by a swarm of flies, and we used to have to chase after them for incredible distances. Curiously enough, they were always more inclined to wander off on their own, or start fighting among themselves, than to forage for food. But this picturesque behaviour was no pleasure to us. We knew that on our return the fullness of their bellies would be carefully inspected to find out how well they had pastured; and woe betide us should the bellies of these rawboned creatures appear inadequately filled!

But woe betide us indeed, if a single head was missing from this devil's own herd! At night, we would run till we were breathless, trying to herd them together; we would lay about them with a big stick, which was not much good, I fear, and certainly did not improve the dispositions of these fantastic beasts. Then we would lead them to water and make them drink vast quantities to make up for the lack of solid stuff in their bellies. We would come back, worn out, with the entire herd. It goes without saying that we would not have dared to come back to the school without having mustered the complete herd. I shudder to think of what one missing head would have cost us!

Such were the dealings we had with our teachers, the black side of our school life: and naturally we could hardly wait for our schooling to be over, for the day when we would receive our famous proficiency certificates that would proclaim to the world that we were 'educated'. Yet when I think of what the pupils in the top form made us suffer, all that I have said about the 'black' side of our school life seems to pale into insignificance. Those older students – I refuse to call them school-fellows – who were older and stronger than we were, and less strictly supervised, persecuted us in every conceivable way. They gave themselves superior airs and had an inflated sense of their own importance – they probably felt that they would never enjoy so much power again – and perhaps they were trying to get a little of their own back for the rough handling they themselves had experienced when they were younger: excessively harsh treatment is perhaps not quite the best method of inculcating good behaviour.

I still remember – my hands and my finger-tips still remember! – what used to lie in store for us on our return to school from the holidays. The guava trees in the school yard would be in full leaf again, and the old leaves would be strewn around in scattered heaps. In places there were even more than just heaps of them: it would be like a muddy sea of leaves.

'Get that all swept up!' the headmaster would tell us. 'I want the whole place cleaned up, at once!'

'At once!' There was enough work there, damned hard work, too, to last us for a week. Especially since the only tools with which we were provided were our hands, our fingers, our nails.

'Now see that it's done properly, and be quick about it,' the headmaster would say to the older pupils, 'or you'll have to answer for it!'

So at an order from the older boys we would all line up like peasants about to reap or glean a field, and we would set to work like members of a chain-gang. In the school yard itself, it wasn't too bad: the guava trees were fairly well spaced; but there was one part where the closely planted trees grew in a hopeless tangle of leaves and branches. The sun could not penetrate here, and the acrid stench of decay lingered in the undergrowth even at the height of summer.

If the work was not going as quickly as the headmaster expected, the big boys, instead of giving us a helping hand, used to find it simpler to whip us with branches pulled from the trees. Now guava wood is regrettably flexible; skilfully handled, the springy switches used to whistle piercingly, and fall like flails of fire on our backsides. Our flesh stung and smarted, while tears of anguish sprang from our eyes and splashed on the rotting leaves at our feet.

In order to avoid these blows, we used to bribe our tyrants with the succulent cakes of Indian corn, the *couscous* made of meat or fish which we used to bring for our midday meal. And if we happened to have any money on us, the coins changed hands at once. If we did not do this, if we were afraid of going home with an empty stomach or an empty purse, the blows were redoubled. They were administered with such furious generosity and with such diabolical gusto that even a deaf mute would have gathered that we were being flogged not so much to spur us on to work, but rather to lash us into a state of submissiveness in which we would be only too glad to give up our food and money.

Occasionally, one of us, worn out by such calculated cruelty, would have the courage to complain to the headmaster. He would of course be very angry, but the punishment he inflicted on the older boys was always negligible – nothing compared to what they had done to us. And the fact is that however much we complained, our situation did not improve in the slightest. Perhaps we should have let our parents know what was going on, but somehow we never dreamed of doing so; I don't know whether it was loyalty or pride that kept us silent, but I can see now that we were foolish to keep quiet about it, for such beatings were utterly foreign to our nature, to the most fundamental and secret principles of our character, and completely at variance with our passion for independence and equality.

But one day, one of my little school-mates, Kouyaté Karamoko, who had just been brutally assaulted, declared openly that he had had enough of this sort of thing. Kouyaté was extremely small and thin, so small and thin that we used to tell him jokingly that he couldn't have any stomach, or at least one only as big as a bird's : a gizzard. Moreover, Kouyaté did nothing to develop his little gizzard or whatever it was that served him for a stomach : he only liked sour, acid things, and citrus fruits : at lunch break, he wasn't happy unless he could exchange his *couscous* for guavas, oranges or lemons. But if Kouyaté was to be deprived even of fruit, it was obvious that his gizzard or whatever it was would finally become even smaller : like the stomach of a grasshopper, perhaps. Now the older boys' insistent demands forced Kouyaté into periods of rigorous fasting. That day, his frustrated passion for sour fruit and also the weals on his buttocks, turned Kouyaté into a rebel.

'Yes, I've had enough of it !' he said to me, sniffing through his tears. 'D'you hear ? I've had enough ! I'm going to tell my father.'

'You keep quiet,' I said. 'Telling your father won't do us any good.'

'Do you really believe that ?'

'Don't forget, the big boys . . .'

But he would not let me finish.

'I'm going to tell him!' he cried.

'Hush, don't shout like that!'

We were working in the same row, and he was the nearest to me in it: I was afraid that this outburst would bring another flogging from the big boys.

'You know what sort of a man my father is, don't you?' he said.

'Yes, of course.'

Kouyaté's father was one of the most venerated praise-singers of the district. He was an educated man, welcome everywhere, though he no longer practised his art; he was a kind of emeritus praise-singer, and very proud of his position.

'But your father's an old man now,' I said.

'He's tough!' said Kouyaté proudly.

He drew his thin little body up to its full height.

'You make me laugh sometimes!' I said.

Whereupon he began to whimper again.

'Oh, well, do as you like!' I told him.

The next day, Kouyaté had no sooner entered the school yard than he went over to Himourana, the big boy who had thrashed him so mercilessly the day before.

'My father is most anxious to meet the boy who has been kindest to me in the top class, and I thought of you at once. Can you come and share our dinner this evening?'

'You bet I can!' answered Himourana, who was as stupid as he was brutal, and probably as greedy as he was stupid.

That evening, at the appointed time, this big bully Himourana showed up at Kouyaté's compound. Now this compound is one of the best-guarded ones in Kouroussa: it has only one gate, and the fence around it, instead of being made of woven reeds, is constructed of mud bricks, with pieces of broken glass bottles fixed to the top. It could be entered and left only with the permission of the master of the house. Kouyaté's father came in person to open the gate, and when Himourana was inside, he carefully bolted it.

'Would you care to sit down in the courtyard?' he said. 'Our whole family is expecting you.'

Himourana took a quick look at the pots and pans, which seemed to give ample promise of a succulent repast, and sat down with the rest of the family, eager for the compliments that he felt sure were about to be addressed to him. But Kouyaté got up and pointed at him.

'My father,' he said, 'this is the big boy who never stops beating me, and takes my food and my money!'

'Well, well,' said Kouyaté's father, 'that's not a nice thing to say about him. Are you sure you're telling me the truth?'

'I swear by Allah!' said Kouyaté.

'So it must be the truth,' said his father.

And he turned towards Himourana.

'Well, young man, it's time you gave an explanation of your strange behaviour. Have you anything to say in your defence? Be quick: I haven't much time to spare, but I don't want to be uncharitable.'

It was as if a thunderbolt had dropped at Himourana's feet – he couldn't have been more dumbfounded: he had obviously not heard a word of what Kouyaté's father had said to him. As soon as he had recovered a little from his surprise, his one thought was to get away; this was obviously his best course, but it needed a stupid bully like Himourana to imagine he could escape from such a well-guarded compound. He had not run more than a few steps before he was caught.

'Now, sir,' said Kouyaté's father, 'listen carefully to what I have to say to you; get this into your head, once and for all: I do not send my son to school to learn how to become the slave of boys like you !'

And thereupon Himourana felt himself lifted in the air by his feet and arms – everything had been carefully planned – and held in a convenient position, while, despite his screams, Kouyaté's father laid into him, belabouring his bare backside with his cattle-whip. Then he was allowed to run away, shamefaced, with his tail on fire, like a scalded cat.

Next day, the story of Himourana's beating spread like wildfire. It created a real scandal. Nothing like that had ever happened before, so that we found it hard to realise that it had actually taken place, although all felt we had been avenged by the action taken by Kouyaté's father. The big boys of the two top classes held a meeting and decided that Kouyaté as well as his sister Mariama would be sent to Coventry, and they ordered all of us to send them to Coventry too; but they did not dare lay a finger on Kouyaté or his sister, and at this even the stupidest among us became aware that they were afraid : we suddenly felt that an era had ended and we prepared to breathe the air of liberty again.

At midday, I went up to Kouyaté, having decided to defy the big boys' orders.

'Careful,' said Kouyaté, 'they might beat you for this.'

'I'm not afraid of them !' I said.

I had some oranges for my midday meal, and I gave them to him.

'Thank you,' he said, 'but do go away : I'm afraid they'll beat you.'

I had no time to reply : I could see several of the big boys coming towards us, and I hesitated an instant, uncertain whether to stand up to them or to run away. I decided to stand up to them. Had I not already begun to do so ? But suddenly I felt my head reeling under their blows, and I took to my heels. I did not stop until I had reached the edge of the school yard, then I began to cry, more with rage than pain. When I had pulled myself together a little, I saw Fanta sitting beside me.

'What do *you* want?' 'I said.

'I've brought you a wheat cake,' she replied.

I took it and ate it almost without realising what I was doing, though Fanta's mother was renowned as the best cake-maker in the district. I got up and drank some water and washed my face. Then I came back and sat down again.

'I don't like you to come and sit beside me when I'm crying,' I said.

'Were you crying?' she asked. 'I didn't notice.'

I looked at her. She was lying. Why was she lying? Obviously to spare my pride: I smiled at her.

'Do you want another wheat cake?' she asked.

'No,' I replied. 'I couldn't eat another one: I feel sick with anger. Don't you?'

'Yes,' she said.

There were suddenly tears in her eyes.

'Oh, I hate them!' I said. 'You can't imagine how much I hate them! Listen: I'm going to leave this school. I'm going to try and grow up fast, then I'll come back, and for every beating I've received I'll pay them back a hundredfold! Yes,' I said, 'that's what I'll do!'

She stopped crying, and looked up admiringly at me.

That evening, I went and spoke to my father under the veranda.

'Father,' I said. 'I can't go to school any more.'

'What?' said my father.

'No,' I said, 'I can't go back.'

But by this time the scandal had had time to go the rounds of the compounds in Kouroussa.

'What's going on in that school?' my father asked.

'I'm afraid of the big boys,' I said.

'I thought you weren't afraid of anyone?'

'I am : I'm afraid of the big boys.'

'What have they been doing to you?'

'They take everything I've got! They take my money and they take my food.'

'Do they now?' said my father. 'And do they beat you?'

'Do they beat me!' I said bitterly.

'Very well, then, I'll come and have a word with those bullies tomorrow. Will that do?'

'Yes, Father.'

The next morning my father and his apprentices came with me to the school gate. Each time a big boy approached, my father said to me :

'Is that one of them?'

I always said no, even though many of them *had* whipped me and robbed me; I was waiting for my most persistent attacker to appear. When I saw him coming I said in a loud voice :

'That's the one who beats me the most!'

At once the apprentices threw themselves upon him and stripped him naked, and began to beat him so hard that my father had in the end to restrain them. Then my father said to the big boy who stood there with a frightened look in his eyes :

'I shall have a word with the headmaster about you. I should like to know if the pupils in the top forms of this school are here solely for the purpose of beating up the younger boys and stealing their money.'

That day, there was no longer any question of sending Kouyaté and his sister to Coventry : they mingled with us freely, and none of the big boys dared raise his voice in protest or lift a finger to us. Was a new era beginning? It felt like it. The big boys kept to themselves. And as we kept well away from them and were more numerous than they were, it almost looked as if it was the big boys who had been sent to Coventry by us; they looked embarrassed. Indeed, they were in a rather unpleasant situation : their parents had not known about their tyrannical cruelty; if they got to know about it, and there was now every likelihood that the whole thing would become public, the big boys would have to endure all kinds of scoldings and punishments.

In the afternoon, at the end of school, my father came as he had said he would. The headmaster was in the school yard, surrounded by teachers. My father went up to him, and, without even stopping to wish him good day, said :

'Do you know what's been going on in this school?'

'Everything is going as it should,' said the headmaster.

'It is, is it?' said my father. 'Are you not aware of the fact that the big boys beat the little ones, that they steal their money and take their food? Are you blind, or do you not wish to see what's going on?'

'I'll thank you to mind your own business!' said the headmaster.

'And this is not my own business?' said my father. 'Is it none of my business when my own son is being treated like a slave in your school?'

'Certainly not.'

'You should not have said that,' said my father. And he went right up to the headmaster.

'Do you think you'll beat me up as your apprentices beat up one of my pupils this morning?' cried the headmaster.

And he hit out with his fists; but although he was stronger, he was fat and his fat impeded rather than helped him; and my father, who was thin, but active and supple, had no difficulty in dodging his blows and setting about him in no uncertain fashion. My father got him down on the ground and was punching him for all he was worth: I don't know what might have happened if the teachers had not dragged him off.

The headmaster was feeling his jaw and didn't say a word. My father dusted himself down, then took me by the hand. He went out of the school yard without a word to anyone, and I marched proudly back to our compound with him. But towards evening, when I went for a walk in the town, I could hear folks saying as I passed by:

'Look! That's the schoolboy whose father went and beat up the headmaster in his own school yard!'

And suddenly I didn't feel nearly so proud. This scandal was not the same sort of thing as Kouyaté's father had started. It had taken place in front of the teachers and the pupils, and the headmaster himself had been the victim. No, this wasn't at all the same sort of thing; and I imagined that now I would be expelled. I ran back to our compound and said to my father:

'Why did you beat him? Now they won't want me back at school, I know.'

'I thought you said that you didn't want to go back to school?' said my father.

And he laughed out loud.

'But, Father, it's no laughing matter!' I said.

'You go to sleep and forget all about it, you little silly. If we don't hear the put-put of a certain motor bicycle outside the gate of the compound tomorrow, I shall complain to the district supervisor.'

But my father did not need to make this complaint, and I was not expelled, for, the next day, a little before nightfall, the headmaster's motor bike chugged up to the gate of our compound. The headmaster came in, and everybody, my father included, went to meet him, and greeted him amiably with:

'Good evening, sir.'

He offered the headmaster a chair, and my father and he sat down, while, at a sign from my father, the rest of us withdrew. The interview seemed to be a very cordial one; indeed it must have been, for from then on, my sister and I took part in no more forced labour at school.

Yet the scandal could not be hushed up entirely. A few months later the headmaster was forced to resign owing to a petition signed by all of the parents. But meanwhile the rumour had got around that he was using some of the bigger lads as house-boys for the convenience of his wives. These pupils had been boarded with him so that they might enjoy special attention, and their board had been paid for with cattle. I don't know all the ins and outs of the affair; I only know that this was the last straw that broke the camel's back, and that we were never again bullied by the big boys.

Seven

I WAS growing up. The time had come for me to join the society of the uninitiated. This rather mysterious society – and at that age, it was very mysterious to me, though not very secret – contained all the young boys, all the uncircumcised of twelve, thirteen or fourteen years of age, and it was run by our elders, whom we called the big 'Kondéns'. I joined it one evening before the feast of Ramadan.

As soon as the sun had gone down, the tom-tom had begun to beat. Even though it was being played in a remote part of the compound, the notes had roused me at once, had struck my breast, had struck right at my heart, just as if Kodoké, our best player, had been playing for me alone. A little later, I had heard faintly the shrill voices of boys accompanying the tom-tom with their cries and singing . . . Yes, the time had come for me . . .

It was the first time I had spent the feast of Ramadan at Kouroussa; until this year, my grandmother had always insisted on my spending it with her, at Tindican. All that morning, and even more so in the afternoon, I had been in a state of great agitation, with everyone busy preparing for the festival, bumping into and pushing each other and asking me to help. Outside, the uproar was just as bad : Kouroussa is the chief town of our region, and all the canton chiefs, attended by their musicians, make it a custom to gather here for the festival. From the gateway to the compound I had watched them pass by, with the companies of praise-singers, balaphonists and guitarists, drum and tom-tom players. Until now I had only been thinking of the festival and of the sumptuous feast that awaited me – but now, there was something quite different in the wind.

The screaming crowd that surrounded Kodoké and his tom-tom was getting nearer. It was going from one compound to another; it would stop for a moment in each compound where there was a boy of an age, as I was, to join the society, and it would take the boy away. That is why it was so slow in coming, yet so sure, so ineluctable; as sure, as ineluctable as the fate that awaited me.

What fate? My meeting with 'Kondén Diara'.

Now I was not unaware who Kondén Diara was : often my mother, and at times my uncles, had talked of him only too much, had threatened me only too often with Kondén Diara, that terrible bogeyman, that 'lion that eats up little boys.' And here was Kondén Diara – but was he a man? Was he an animal? Was he not rather half-man, half-animal? My friend Kouyaté believed he was more man than beast – here was Kondén

Diara leaving the dim world of hearsay, here he was taking on flesh and blood, yes, and prowling, roused by Kodoké's tom-tom, around the dark town! This night was to be the night of Kondén Diara.

I could hear now very plainly the beating of the tom-tom – Kodoké was much nearer – I could hear perfectly the chanting and the shouts that rose into the dark, I could make out distinctly the rather hollow, crisp, well-marked beats of the coros, that are a kind of miniature canoe, and are beaten with a bit of wood. I was standing at the entrance to the compound, waiting. I, too, was holding, ready to play it, my coro, with the stick clutched nervously in my hand; I was waiting, hidden by the shadow of the hut; I was waiting, filled with a dreadful anxiety, my eyes searching the blackness.

'Well?' asked my father.

He had crossed the workshop without my hearing him.

'Are you afraid?'

'A little,' I replied.

He laid his hand on my shoulder.

'It's all right. Don't worry.'

He drew me to him, and I could feel his warmth; it warmed me, too, and I began to feel less frightened, my heart did not beat so fast.

'I, too, went through this test,' said my father.

'What happens to you?' I asked.

'Nothing you need really be afraid of, nothing you cannot overcome by your own will-power. Remember: you have to control your fear, you have to control your self. Kondén Diara will not take you away; he will roar; but he won't do more than roar. You won't be frightened, now, will you?'

'I'll try not to be.'

'Even if you are frightened, do not show it.'

He went away, and I began waiting again, and the

disturbing uproar came nearer and nearer. Suddenly I saw the crowd emerging from the dark and rushing towards me; Kodoké, his tom-tom slung over one shoulder, was marching at their head, followed by the drummers.

I ran back quickly into the yard, and, standing in the middle of it, I awaited, with as much pluck as I could muster, the awful invasion. I did not have long to wait: the crowd was upon me, it was spreading tumultuously all round me, overwhelming me with shouts and cries and beating tom-toms, beating drums. It formed a circle, and I found myself in the centre, alone, curiously isolated, still free and yet already captive. Inside the circle, I recognised Kouyaté and others, many of them friends of mine who had been collected as the crowd moved on, collected as I was to be, as I already was: and it seemed to me they were none of them looking very happy – but was I any more than they were? I began to beat my coro, as they were doing; perhaps I was beating it with less confidence than they.

At this point young girls and women joined the circle and began to dance; young men and adolescents, stepping out of the crowd, moved into the circle too and began to dance facing the women. The men sang, the women clapped their hands. Soon the only ones left to form the circle were the uncircumcised boys. They, too, began to sing – they were not allowed to dance – and as they sang, sang in unison, they forgot their anxiety; I, too, mingled my voice with theirs. When, having formed began to sing – they were not allowed to dance – and as a circle again, the crowd left our compound, I went with it, almost willingly, beating my coro with great enthusiasm. Kouyaté was on my right.

Towards the middle of the night, our tour of the town and the collection of uncircumcised boys was finished: we had arrived at the farthest outskirts of the compounds, and in front of us lay only the dark scrub-land. Here the

women and young girls left us; then the grown men left
us. We were alone with the older boys, or should I say
'delivered over' to the older boys – for I remember
the often rather disagreeable natures and rarely pleasant
manners of those older ones.

The women and young girls now hurried back to
their dwellings. Actually, they cannot have been any
more at ease than we were; I know for a fact that not
one of them would have ventured to leave town on this
night. In a short while, when Kondén Diara would begin
to roar, they would not be able to stop shaking with
fright; they would all be shaking in their shoes, and
making sure the doors were all properly barred. For
them, as for us, though in a much less significant way,
this night would be the night of Kondén Diara.

As soon as our elders had made sure that no intruder
was present to disturb the mysteriousness of the ceremony, we left the town behind and entered the bush by a
path which leads to a sacred place where each year the
initiation takes place. The place is well known : it is
situated under an enormous bombax tree, a hollow at
the junction of the river Komoni and the river Niger.
At normal times, it is not forbidden to go there; but
certainly it has not always been so, and some emanation
from the past I never knew seemed to hover around the
huge trunk of the bombax tree : I think that a night
such as the one we were going through must certainly
have resurrected a part of that past.

We were walking in silence, closely hemmed in by
our elders. Perhaps they were afraid we might escape?
It looked like it. I do not think, however, that the idea of
escape had occurred to any of us; the night, and that
particular night, seemed impenetrable. Who knew where
Kondén Diara had his lair? Who knew where he was
prowling? But was it not right here, near the hollow?
Yes, it must be here. And if we had to face him –

and certainly we *had* to face him – it would surely be better to do so in a crowd, in this jostling group that seemed to make us all one, and seemed like a last refuge from the peril that was approaching.

Nevertheless, however intimate our jostling proximity to one another, and however careful the vigilance of our elders, it could not be denied that the silence of our progress, after the recent uproar, as we marched far from the huts through the wan moonlight, and even more, the thought of the sacred place towards which we were going, and finally and above all, the concealed presence of Kondén Diara – all these things filled us with terror.

Just before we reached the hollow, we saw flames leap up from a huge wood fire that the bushes had hidden from us until then. Kouyaté squeezed my arm and I knew he was referring to the fire. I quickened my steps – we all quickened our steps – and the crimson radiance of the fire enveloped us. We had a harbour now, a kind of haven from the night : a huge blaze, and, at our backs, the bombax tree's enormous trunk. Oh! It was a precarious haven! But however poor, it was infinitely better than the silence and the dark, the sullen silence of the dark. We assembled beneath the bombax tree. The ground beneath had been cleared of reeds and tall grasses.

Our elders suddenly shouted, 'Kneel!'

We at once fell to our knees.

'Heads down!'

We lowered our heads.

'Lower than that!'

We bent our heads right to the ground, as if in prayer.

'Now hide your eyes!'

We don't have to be told twice; we shut our eyes tight and press our hands over them. For would we not die of fright and horror if we should see, or so much as catch a glimpse of Kondén Diara? Our elders walk up and down behind us and in front of us, to make sure that we had all obeyed their orders to the letter. Woe to him who would have the audacity to disobey! He would be cruelly whipped.

Now that we are on our knees with our foreheads to the ground and our hands pressed over our eyes, Kondén Diara's roaring suddenly bursts out.

We were expecting to hear this hoarse roar, we were not expecting any other sound, but it takes us by surprise, and shatters us, freezes our hearts with its unexpectedness. And it is not only a lion, it is not only Kondén Diara roaring: there are ten, twenty, perhaps thirty lions that take their lead from him, uttering their terrible roars and surrounding the hollow; ten or thirty lions separated from us by a few yards only and that the great wood fire will perhaps not always keep at bay; lions of every size and every age – we can tell that by the way they roar – from the very oldest lions to the very youngest cubs. No, not one of us would dream of venturing to open an eye, not one! Not one of us would dare to lift his head from the ground, he would rather bury it in the earth. And I bend down as far as I can: we all bend down farther, we bend our knees as much as we can, we keep our backs as low as possible; I make myself, we all make ourselves as small as we can.

'You must not be afraid!' I told myself. 'You must conquer your fear! Your father told you to overcome your fear!' But how could I *not* be afraid? Even inside the town, far from this clearing, women and children were trembling and crouching in their huts; they were listening to Kondén Diara roaring, many of them were stopping their ears so as not to hear him roaring; a few bolder spirits might be getting up – it needs some courage to leave one's bed just now – to make quite sure once more that their hut door is closed, to make quite sure that it is securely bolted and barred; nevertheless they are still as frightened as anyone else. How can I possibly not give way to my terror, I who am within reach of the monster? If it so pleased him, he could leap right through the fire and plunge his terrible claws into my flesh!

Not for a single instant do I doubt the presence of the monster. Who could assemble such a numerous herd, hold such a nocturnal revel, if not Kondén Diara? 'He alone,' I said to myself, 'he alone has such power over lions . . . Keep away, Kondén Diara! Keep away! Go back into the bush! . . .' But Kondén Diara went on with his revels, and sometimes it seemed to me that he roared right over my own head, right in my own ears even. 'Keep away, I implore thee, Kondén Diara!'

What was it my father had said? 'Kondén Diara roars; but he won't do more than roar; he will not take you away . . .' Yes, something like that. But is it true, really true? There is also a rumour that Kondén Diara sometimes pounces with fearsome claws on someone or other and carries him far away, far, far away into the depths of the bush; and then, days and days afterwards, months or even years later, quite by chance a huntsman may discover some whitened bones . . . And do not people also die of fright? . . . Ah! how I wish this roaring would stop! How I wish . . . How I wish I was far away from this clearing, back in the compound, in the warm security of the hut! . . . Will this roaring never end? . . . 'Go away Kondén Diara! Go away! . . . Stop roaring . . .' Oh! those roars! . . . I feel as if I can bear them no longer . . .

Whereupon, suddenly, they stop! They stop just as they had begun, so suddenly, in fact, that I feel only reluctant relief. Is it over? Really over? . . . Is it not just a temporary interruption? . . . No, I dare not feel relieved just yet. And then suddenly the voice of one of the older boys rings out:

'Get up!'

I heave a sigh of relief. This time, it's really over. We look at one another: I look at Kouyaté and the others. If there was only a little more light . . . But the light from the fire is sufficient: great drops of sweat are still beading our foreheads; yet the night is chill . . . Yes, we were afraid. We were not able to conceal our fear . . .

A new command rang out, and we sat down in front of the fire. Now our elders begin our initiation; all night long they will teach us the songs of the uncircumcised; and we must remain quite still, repeating the words after them, singing the melody after them; there we sit, as if we were in school again, attentive, very attentive, and very obedient.

Our lessons ended with the dawn.

My legs and arms were numb; I worked my joints and rubbed my legs for a while, but my blood still flowed slowly; I was really worn out, and I was cold. Looking round me, I could not understand why I shook with fear during the night: the first rays of dawn were falling so gently, so reassuringly, on the bombax tree, on the clearing; the sky looked so pure! Who could believe that only a few hours ago a whole herd of lions, led by Kondén Diara himself, had been angrily roaring among these tall reeds and grasses, separated from us only by a wood fire which now was almost dead? No one would have believed it, and I should have doubted the evidence of my own ears and thought I was waking up from a bad dream, if one or the other of my companions had not now and then cast a suspicious glance at the tallest grasses.

For what were those long white threads which hung from, or rather, waved from the top of the bombax tree and which appeared to write on the sky the direction in which the town lay? I had not time to wonder very long at this: our elders were re-grouping us; and, because the majority were almost walking in their sleep, the operation was carried out not without difficulty, not without shouts and some rough treatment. Finally we started off back to the town singing our new songs, and we sang them with unbelievably care-free abandon : even so the steed that scents the approaching stable suddenly quickens his pace, however weary he may be. When we reached the first compound, the presence of the long white threads struck me once more: all the principal huts bore these threads on the summit of the roof.

'Do you see those white threads?' I said to Kouyaté.

'I can see them. They are always there after the ceremony in the clearing.'

'Who puts them there?'

Kouyaté shrugged his shoulders.

'That's where they come from,' I said, pointing to the distant bombax tree.

'Someone must have climbed up.'

'Who could possibly climb up a bombax tree?'

'I don't know.'

'Could anyone possibly get his arms round such a huge trunk?' I said. 'And even if he could, how could he hoist himself up on a bark covered with all those thorns? You're talking nonsense. Can't you imagine what a job it would be, just to reach the first branches?'

'How should I know any more than you?' said Kouyaté.

'But this is the first time I've attended this sort of ceremony. Whereas you . . .'

I did not finish the sentence; we had reached the main square of the town. I stared in amazement at the bombax trees of the market-place; they, too, were ornamented with the same white threads. All but the humblest huts, indeed, and all the big trees were tied to one another by these white threads, whose focal point was the enormous bombax tree in the clearing, the sacred place marked by the bombax tree.

'The swallows tie them on,' said Kouyaté suddenly.

'Swallows? Are you crazy?' I said. 'Swallows do not fly by night.'

I questioned one of the older boys who was walking beside us.

'It is our great chief who does it,' he said. 'Our chief turns himself into a swallow during the night. He flies from tree to tree and from hut to hut, and all these threads are tied on in less time than it takes to tell.'

'Does he fly from tree to tree?' I asked. 'Can he fly like a swallow?'

'Why, yes, of course! He is a real swallow, he can fly as swiftly as any swallow. Everybody knows that!'

'There! What did I tell you?' said Kouyaté.

I did not say another word. The night of Kondén Diara was a strange night, a terrible and miraculous night, a night that passed all understanding.

As on the previous evening, we went from one compound to another, preceded by tom-toms and drums, and our companions left one after another as they reached their homes. Whenever we passed a compound where someone whose courage had failed him had refused to join us, a mocking chant rose from our ranks.

I got back to our compound, completely exhausted, but very satisfied with myself: I had taken part in the ceremony of the lions! Even if I had not put up much of a show when Kondén Diara was roaring, that was my own affair; I could keep that to myself. I passed triumphantly over the threshold of our dwelling-place.

The festival of Ramadan was beginning. In the yard, I saw my parents, who were dressed ready to go to the mosque.

'Here you are at last,' said my mother.

'Here I am,' said I proudly.

'What kind of a time is this to come home?' she said, pressing me to her bosom. 'The night is over, and you haven't had a wink of sleep.'

'The ceremony did not finish until break of day,' I said.

'I know, I know,' she said. 'All you men are crazy.'

'What about the lions?' asked my father. 'What about Kondén Diara?'

'I heard them,' I replied. 'They were very close; they were as near to me as I am to you now. There was only the fire between us.'

'It's crazy,' said my mother. 'Go to bed, you're dropping with sleep.'

She turned towards my father:

'I ask you, where's the sense in all that?'

'Well, it's the custom,' said my father.

'I don't like such customs,' she said. 'Young boys should not have to stay awake all night.'

'Were you afraid?' asked my father. Should I admit that I was very frightened?

'Of course he was afraid,' said my mother.

'Only a little,' said my father.

'Go to bed,' said my mother. 'If you don't get some sleep now, you'll fall asleep during the feast.'

It is only after having taken part several times in the lion ceremony that we begin vaguely to understand what goes on, but we still keep it a secret: we only talk about what we have guessed to those of our companions who have shared the same experience; and even so the real secret is not revealed to us until the day of our final initiation into manhood.

Later I got to know who Kondén Diara was, and I learnt also that the dangers were non-existent. But I only learnt these things when the time had come for me to learn them. As long as we are not circumcised, as long as we have not attained that second life that is our

true existence, we are told nothing, and we can find out
nothing.

No, they were not real lions that were roaring in the
clearing, for it was the older boys, plainly and simply
the older boys. They create the roaring sound with
small boards, thick at the centre, sharp at the edges:
the board is ellipsoidal in shape and very small; there
is a hole on one side that permits it to be tied to a string.
The older boys swing it round like a swing, and, to in-
crease the speed of the gyrations, they, too, turn with
it. The board cuts through the air and produces a roaring sound similar to a lion's roar; the smallest boards
imitate the roaring of lion cubs; the biggest ones, the
roaring of fully-grown lions.

It's childishly simple. What is not so childish is the
effect produced at night on someone who does not expect it: the heart freezes! If it was not for the far
greater fear of finding themselves lost in the bush, the
terror it creates would make the boys run away.

But if Kondén Diara's roaring is easily explained, the
presence of the long white threads binding the great
bombax tree in the sacred clearing to the tallest trees
and the principal houses of the town is less easily explained. For my own part, I never succeeded in obtain-
ing an explanation: at the time when I might have
obtained it, that is, when I should have taken my place
among the older boys who conducted the ceremony, I
was no longer living at Kouroussa. All I know is that
these threads are spun from cotton and that bamboo rods
are used to tie them to the summits of the bombax tree.

Our bombax trees are very big, and it is difficult to
imagine perches sixty feet high; such structures would
certainly collapse, no matter how carefully they had
been put together. Moreover, I do not see how the
summit of these thorny trees could be reached by climbing. There is, of course, a kind of belt which tree-

climbers use; the belt is tied round the tree and the climber gets inside it, placing the belt against the small of his back, then climbs by a series of jerks, pressing against the trunk with his feet: but such a proceeding is quite unthinkable, given the dimensions of the trunk of our enormous bombax trees.

Or why not plainly and simply use a sling? I do not know. A good slinger can work miracles. Perhaps it is this sort of miracle which would account for the inexplicable presence of white threads at the summit of the bombax trees. But I can come to no final decision about it.

All I know is that the older ones who tie these threads to the tops of trees must be extraordinarily careful not to leave their bamboo rods lying about: they must not give themselves away! Now all it would need would be a bamboo rod left carelessly at the foot of one of the trees to give the show away to the women and children. That is why, as soon as the threads have been tied, the first thing they do is to hide away their rods and poles. The usual hiding-places are in the thatch of a roof or in remote parts of the bush. And in this way no material evidence remains of these manifestations of the power of Kondén Diara.

But what about the men? What about those who *do* know?

They just won't breathe a single word about it, they keep their knowledge a close secret. Not only do they keep women and children in a state of uncertainty and terror, they also warn them to keep the doors of their huts firmly barred.

I am not unaware that such conduct might appear strange, but it is absolutely true. If the ceremony of the lions has the character of a game, if it is for the most part pure mystification, yet it has one important feature: it is a test, a training in hardship, a rite; the prelude to a

tribal rite, and for the present that is all one can say . . .
It is obvious that if the secret was given away, the ceremony would lose much of its power. Certainly the teaching which follows the roaring of Kondén Diara would
remain the same; but nothing would remain of the trial
by fear, that occasion when there is given to every boy
the opportunity to overcome his own baser nature; nothing would remain of the necessary preparation for the
painful tribal rite of circumcision. But at the moment
of writing, is there any part of the rite that still remains?

The secret . . . Do we still have secrets?

Eight

LATER ON, I went through an ordeal much more frightening than Kondén Diara, this time a really dangerous
ordeal whose nature is far removed from that of any
game: circumcision.

I was then in my final scholarship year: I, too, was at
last among the big boys, whom we had so detested when
we were in the infants' class because they used to extort
food and money from us and used to beat us; here we
were taking their place, and the hardships we had en-
dured at their hands were now happily abolished.

But it was not enough simply to be in the big boys'
class: we had to be 'big' in every sense of the word,
and that meant we had to become men. But I was still
a child: I was considered not to have reached the age
of discretion yet! Among my companions, most of
whom were circumcised, I was still looked upon as a
child. I suppose I was a little younger than they, or was
it that my repeated visits to Tindican had delayed my
initiation? I do not remember. Whatever the reason,

I had now reached the age at which I, too, must be re-born, at which I, too, must abandon my childhood and my innocence, and become a man.

It was not without misgivings that I approached this transition from childhood to manhood; the thought of it really caused me great distress, as it did those who were to share the ordeal. Of course, the ceremony itself, the visible part of it at least, was familiar to us, for each year we would watch the candidates for circumcision dancing in the town's main square. But the important, the essential part of the ceremony remained a secret, and we only had a very vague notion of how it was carried out, though we knew that the operation itself was a painful one.

The public ceremony differs completely from the secret one. The public ceremony is one of rejoicing. It is the occasion of a great festival, a very noisy festival in which the whole town participates and which lasts several days. And it is almost as if by dint of noise and activity and dancing and merry-making people were trying to make us forget our anxiety about the coming ordeal, and its very real physical pain.

But however great the anxiety, however certain the pain, no one would have dreamed of running away from the ordeal – no more than one would have dreamed of running away from the ordeal of the lions – and I for my own part never entertained such thoughts. I wanted to be born, to be born again. I knew perfectly well that I was going to be hurt, but I wanted to be a man and it seemed to me that nothing could be too painful if, by enduring it, I was to come to a man's estate. My companions felt the same; like myself, they were pre-pared to pay for it with their blood. Our elders before us had paid for it thus; those who were born after us would pay for it in their turn. Why should we be spared? Life itself would spring from the shedding of our blood.

That year, I danced for a whole week in the main square of Kouroussa the dance of the *soli,* which is the dance of those who are to be circumcised. Every afternoon my companions and I would go to the dancing-place, wearing a cap and a boubou which reached to our heels, a much longer boubou than is generally worn, and split up the sides; the cap, a skull-cap, was decorated with a pompom that hung down at the back; and this was our first man's hat. The women and girls would come running to the gates of their compounds to watch us go by; then they would follow closely on our heels, decked in their holiday finery. The tom-tom would throb, and we would dance in the square until we were ready to drop. And as the week wore on, the dances grew longer and the crowds grew bigger.

My boubou, like that of my companions, was of a brownish-red colour, a colour on which bloodstains would not show too clearly. It had been specially woven for the ceremony, and had first of all been white; the masters of the ceremonies had then dyed it with dyes made from the bark of trees, after which they had plunged it into the muddy water of a brushwood pool. The boubou, in order to obtain the desired tone, had been left to soak for several weeks, perhaps because of some ritual reason which I forget. The cap, apart from the pompom, which remained white, had been treated in the same fashion.

We would dance, as I was saying, until we were out of breath; but we were not the only ones dancing: the whole town would dance with us! In our country, all dances have this cumulative tendency, because each beat of the tom-tom has an almost irresistible appeal. Soon those who were just spectators would be dancing too; they would crowd into the open space, and, though they did not mix with our group, they would take an intimate part in our revels, outdoing us in frenzy, men as well as women, women as well as girls; though the women and girls kept strictly apart from us in their dancing.

While I was dancing, my boubou, split from top to bottom at each side, would reveal the brightly-coloured silk handkerchief which I had knotted round my loins. I was quite aware of this and did nothing to prevent it; in fact I did all I could to show it off. This was because we each wore a similar handkerchief, more or less colourful, more or less ornate, which we had received from our acknowledged sweetheart. She would make us a present of it for the ceremony, and it was generally taken from her own head. As the handkerchief cannot pass unnoticed, as it is the one personal note that distinguishes the common uniform, and as its design, like its colour, makes it easily identified, there is in the wearing of it a kind of public manifestation of a relationship – a purely child-like relationship, it goes without saying – which the present ceremony may break for ever, or, as the case may be, transform into something less innocent and more lasting. Now if our so-called sweetheart was in the least pretty and consequently desirable, we would swing our hips with great abandon, the better to make our boubou fly from side to side, and thus show off our handkerchief to greater advantage. At the same time we would keep our ears open to catch anything that might be said about us, about our sweetheart and about our good fortune; but our ears caught very little, for the music was deafening; and there was extraordinary animation in the tightly-packed crowds all round the square.

From time to time a man would break through the crowd and come towards us. It would generally be an older man, often a person of some consequence who was on friendly terms with, or had obligations towards one of our families. The man would indicate that he wished to speak; the tom-toms would stop, and the dancing would be interrupted for a moment. We would gather round him. Thereupon the man would address himself to one or the other of us in a very loud voice.

'O thou!' he would say, 'hearken unto me. Thy family has always been loved by my family; thy grandfather is the friend of my father, thy father is my friend, and thou art the friend of my son. I come here this day that I may testify these things in public. Let every man here know that we are friends, and that we shall ever remain so. And as a symbol of this lasting friendship, and in order to show my gratitude for the goodwill that thy father and thy grandfather have always shown to me and mine, I make thee this gift of an ox on the occasion of thy circumcision.'

We would all applaud him; the entire assembly would applaud him. Many of the older men, all of them friends indeed, would come forward like this and make an announcement of what gifts they were going to present us with. Each one would make an offering in accordance with his means, and the spirit of rivalry would often make it beyond his means. If it was not an ox, it would be a sack of rice, or millet or maize.

For the great feast of the circumcision is the occasion of a great banquet attended by numerous guests; a banquet so enormous that, despite the number of guests, there is enough for days and days before the end is reached. Obviously this entails great expense. So, whoever is a friend of the family of the boy to be circumcised, or is bound to the family by bonds of obligation, makes it a point of honour to contribute to the banquet; and he will help both those who are in need of help and those who are not. That is why, at each circumcision, there is this sudden abundance of gifts and good things.

Did we enjoy this sudden shower of gifts? Not unreservedly; the ordeal that awaited us was not of the kind that whets the appetite. No, we would not be likely to have much appetite, when, the circumcision over, we were invited to take part in the banquet. Though we did not know it by actual experience, we were quite well aware that freshly-circumcised boys had a rather woe-begone look.

This reflection would brutally recall our fears: we would be applauding the donor, and at the same time our thoughts would be returning to the ordeal before us. As I have said: this apprehension in the midst of the general excitement, an excitement in which we, through our dancing, took a major part, was not the least para-doxical aspect of those days. Were we not dancing to forget what we were all dreaming? I can quite believe it. And in truth there were moments when we succeeded. in forgetting it; but anxiety was never far away; there were always fresh occasions for it to spring to life again. Our mothers might make increased sacrifices on our be-half – and certainly they did not fail to do so – yet they were but sorry comfort.

Sometimes one of our mothers, or some other close relative, would join the dance, and often in dancing she would wave aloft the symbol of our class; it was generally a hoe – the peasant class in Guinea is by far the most numerous – and this was to show that the boy who was about to be circumcised was a good labourer.

This was when I saw my father's second wife make her appearance holding aloft an exercise-book and a fountain-pen. I must confess that this gave me no pleasure at all and rather than encouraging me it some-what embarrassed me, although I knew quite well that my second mother was merely observing an old custom, and doing so with the best will in the world, since the exercise-book and the fountain-pen were the symbols of a profession which, in her eyes, was superior to that of a farmer or a mechanic.

My real mother was infinitely more discreet; she simply watched me from a distance; I even noticed that she tried to hide in the crowd. I am sure she was at least as anxious as I was, though she took the greatest trouble to conceal the fact. But for the most part her excitement was such, I mean so all-pervasive, that we had to bear the burden of our uneasiness on our own.

Need I mention that we ate rapidly and without relish? It goes without saying: everything centred on the dancing and on the preparations for the feast. We would go home foot-sore and weary and sleep like logs. In the morning, we could never get up, but lay in bed until the very last moment, when the tom-tom began to summon us. What did it matter if we had no proper meals? We barely had time to eat. We had to wash at top speed, fling on our boubous, jam our caps on our heads, run to the main square and dance. And each day we had to dance more; for we were all dancing now, the whole town was dancing, afternoon and evening – by torchlight in the evening – and on the eve of the ordeal, the town danced all day long, and all night long.

On this final day, we were all worked into a strange kind of excitement. The men who perform this initiation, after having shaved our heads, gathered us together in a hut built apart from the compound. This hut, which was very spacious, would henceforth be our dwelling-place; the spacious square in which it stood was fenced off by such tightwoven osiers that no inquisitive eyes could see through them.

When we entered the hut, we saw our boubous and caps spread on the ground. During the night our boubous had been stitched up the sides except for the arm-holes, so that they covered us completely. As for the caps, they had been transformed into tremendously high bonnets: the material which had originally hung loose had been stiffened by fixing it to a wicker framework. We slipped into our boubous, which made us look rather as if we were in tight sheaths; and now we looked even skinnier than we really were. Then when we had put our long, narrow bonnets on, we looked at each other for a moment; in any other circumstances, we would have certainly burst out laughing : we looked as long and as thin as bamboo poles.

'Go and walk outside for a while,' the men told us; 'you must get used to having your boubous sewn up.'

We took a little walk; but we could not take large strides, for the stitched-up boubous prevented it : it was as if we were in shackles.

We came back to the hut, sat down on the mats and remained there under the supervision of the men. We chattered among ourselves of one thing and another, concealing our uneasiness as best we could; but how could we banish from our minds the thought of to-morrow's ceremony? The uneasiness underlying all our chatter was obvious. The men who were with us were not unaware of this state of mind; whenever, in spite of ourselves, we gave vent to our anxiety, they would be at great pains to reassure us; and in this respect they were quite different from the big boys who performed the ceremony of the lions and who only wanted to frighten us as much as possible.

'Come, don't be afraid,' they said. 'This has happened to every man. Has it done any harm to them? It won't do you any harm either. Now that you are going to become men, conduct yourselves like men; drive away your fears. A man is afraid of nothing.'

But we were still children, all the same; all through that final day, and all through that final night, we would still be children. As I have said before : we were not even considered to have reached the age of discretion. And if that age is a long time in coming, if it does really come only after many years, our 'manhood' will seem all the more premature. We were still children. To-morrow . . . But it was better to think of something else; to think, for example, of the whole town gathered in the main square and dancing happily. But what about us? Were not we, too, about to join the dance?

No. This time, we were going to dance on our own; we were going to dance, and the others were going to watch. At present we were not allowed to mix with other people; our mothers could not even speak to us, let alone touch us. We left the hut, swathed in our long sheaths, and with our enormous bonnets towering on our heads.

As soon as we appeared in the main square, the men ran to meet us. We advanced in single file between two rows of men. Kouyaté's father, a venerable old man with white beard and white hair, thrust through the ranks and placed himself at our head: it was his privilege to show us how to dance the 'coba', a dance kept, like the 'soli', for those who are about to be circumcised, and which is danced only on the eve of circumcision. Kouyaté's father, by virtue of his great age and good name, was the only one who had the right to strike up the chant which accompanies the 'coba'.

I was walking behind him. He told me to put my hands on his shoulders, and then each of us placed his hands on the shoulders of the boy in front of him. When our Indian file had been linked up in this way, the tom-toms and drums suddenly ceased, and everyone was silent, everything became silent and still. Kouyaté's father then drew himself up to his full height, cast his eyes all round him — there was something imperious and noble in his attitude — and, as if it were a command, lifted up his voice in the 'coba' chant:

'*Coba! Aye coba, lama!*'

At once the tom-toms and the drums shattered the silence and we all took up the phrase:

'*Coba! Aye coba, lama!*'

We were walking like Kouyaté's father, legs apart, as

far apart as our boubous would allow, and naturally with very slow steps. As we chanted the words, we would turn our heads, as Kouyaté's father did, to the left, and then to the right; and our high bonnets extended this head movement in a curious way.

'*Coba! Aye coba, lama!*'

We had begun to dance round the square. The older men drew up in two rows as we advanced; and when the last of us had passed through their ranks, they went and formed two little rows again a little farther on for us to pass through. And because we were walking slowly with our legs wide apart, we looked rather like ducks waddling along.

The two ranks of men through which we were moving were thick and tightly packed. The women, behind, would scarcely see more than our high bonnets, and the children obviously even less than that. In previous years, I had only caught glimpses of the tops of the bonnets. But it was enough : the 'coba' is a man's affair. The women . . . No, women had no voice in this matter.

'*Coba! Aye coba, lama!*'

Finally we reached the spot where we had begun our dance. Then Kouyaté's father stopped, the tom-toms and drums fell silent, and we went back to our hut again. We had barely left the square before the dancing and shouting began again.

Three times that day we appeared in the main square to dance the 'coba'; and three times again during the night, by torchlight; and each time the men enclosed us in a living hedge. We did not get any sleep; no one went to bed : the whole town stayed awake and danced all through the night. As we left our hut for the sixth time, dawn was breaking.

'*Coba! Aye coba, lama!*'

Our bonnets still moved in time to the rhythm, our boubous were still stretched over our straddling legs;

but we were beginning to flag, our eyes were burning feverishly and our anxiety was mounting. If we had not been urged on, carried away by the tom-tom beat . . . But it urged us on, carried us away! And we danced on obediently, our heads curiously light from lack of sleep, curiously heavy, too, with thoughts of the fate that was to be ours.

'*Coba! Aye coba, lama!*'

As we came to the end of the dance, dawn began to lighten the main square. This time, we did not go back to our hut; we went immediately into the bush; we went a long way, to where there was no risk of our being disturbed. In the main square the dancing had stopped: the people had all gone home. Nevertheless, a few men followed us out. The rest awaited, in their huts, the ceremonial shots that would announce to all that one more man, one more Malinke, had been born.

We had reached a circular clearing, the ground completely bare. All round, grasses grew high, higher than the men's heads; it was the most secluded spot one could have wished to find. We were lined up, each of us in front of a stone. At the other end of the clearing, the men stood facing us. And we took off our clothes.

I was afraid, terribly afraid, and I needed all my will-power not to show it. All those men standing in front of us and watching us must see nothing of my fear. My companions showed themselves no less brave, and it was absolutely necessary that it should be so; among these men standing in front of us was perhaps our future father-in-law, or a future relative; we dared not let ourselves down now!

Suddenly the operator appeared. We had caught a glimpse of him the night before, when he had performed his dance in the main square. And now, also, I only caught a brief glimpse of him. I had hardly realised he was there, before I saw him standing in front of me.

Was I afraid? I mean, was I even more afraid, had I at that particular moment a fresh access of fear – for I had been beset by fears ever since I had entered the clearing? I did not have time to be afraid. I felt something, like a burn, and I closed my eyes for a fraction of a second. I do not think I cried out. No, I cannot have cried out; I certainly did not have time to do that either. When I opened my eyes, the operator was bent over my neighbour. In a few seconds the dozen or so boys there were that year became men : the operator made me pass from one state to the other, with an indescribable rapidity.

Later, I learned that he was of the Dama family, my mother's family. He had a great reputation; and rightly so, for at the most important festivals he had often circumcised several hundreds of boys in less than an hour; this rapidity was very much appreciated, for it did not prolong the agony. So all parents, all the parents who could, had recourse to him, as he was the most skilful. He would be their guest for the evening, and the guest of the town's most important men, then would go back to the country, where he lived.

As soon as the operation was over, the guns were fired. Our mothers, our relatives in the compounds heard the reports. And while we were being made to sit on the stone in front of us, messengers rushed away, tore through the bush to announce the happy news, arriving bathed in sweat and gasping for breath, so much so that they could hardly deliver their messages to the family that came running to meet them.

'Truly your son has been very brave,' they would shout at last to the mother of the circumcised boy.

And indeed we had all been very brave, we had all very carefully concealed our fear. But we were now perhaps not quite so brave, for the hæmorrhage that follows the operation is abundant, very long, and disturbing: all that blood lost! I watched my blood flowing away and my heart contracted. I thought: 'Is my body going to be entirely emptied of blood?' And I raised imploring eyes to our healer, the 'sema'.

'The blood must flow,' said the 'sema'. 'If it did not flow . . .'

He did not finish the sentence: he was looking at the wound. When he saw that the blood was finally beginning to flow a little less freely, he put on the first bandage. Then he went on to the others.

When the blood had finally ceased flowing, we were dressed in our long boubou again. Apart from a very brief undershirt, this was to be our only article of attire during the weeks of convalescence that were to come. We stood up awkwardly, light-headed and sick at our stomachs. Among the men who had been present at the operation, I saw several who, taking pity on our plight, turned their heads away to hide their tears.

In the town, our parents were making a fuss of the messenger, and loading him with gifts; and the celebrations began again: was it not an occasion for rejoicing over the fortunate outcome of our ordeal, for rejoicing over our new birth? Already friends and neighbours were crowding inside the compounds where the newly circumcised had their homes, and were beginning to dance the 'fady fady' in our honour, the dance of manhood, until the enormous banquet was ready, which would be shared by all.

We, too, were naturally to receive a large share of the dishes. The young men who had conducted the ceremony and who were also our attendants as well as our supervisors, went to seek our share.

Alas! we had seen, and lost, too much blood – its unsavoury smell still seemed to linger in our nostrils – and we all had a touch of fever: we were shaking. We could cast only sour looks on the succulent dishes; they did not tempt us at all, but filled us with revulsion. Of all that extraordinary abundance of viands assembled for our enjoyment we pecked with ridiculously feeble appetite at only one or two dishes : we sat looking at them, sniffing at their savoury smells; we would take a mouthful, then turn our heads away.

At nightfall, we took the road back to the town, escorted by the young men and by our healer. We walked with great care : we could not let the boubou rub against the wound. But sometimes, in spite of our precautions, it would do so, making us cry out with pain; we would stop for a moment, our faces drawn with suffering; the young men would hold us up. It took us a very long time to get back to our hut. When we finally reached it, we were at the end of our tether. We lay down at once on the mats.

We waited for sleep, but it was long in coming, as our fever kept us awake. Our eyes wandered sadly over the walls of the hut. At the thought that we were to live here until our period of convalescence was over – several weeks – in the company of these young men and our healer, we were seized by a kind of despair. Men ! Yes, we were men at last, but what a price to pay ! . . . At last we fell asleep. By the next morning our fever had abated, and we were able to laugh at the sombre thoughts of the night before.

Certainly the life we led in the hut was not the same as the life we led in the compounds; but it was not insupportable and it had its own delights, even though there was constant supervision and the discipline was rather strict, albeit wise and reasonable, with the sole aim of shielding us from anything that might retard our convalescence.

If we were watched closely day and night, and even more closely at night than during the day, it was because we were allowed to lie neither on our side nor on our face; as long as our wound was not properly healed, we could lie only on our backs, and, of course, we were absolutely forbidden to cross our legs. It goes without saying that when we were asleep it was difficult to remain constantly in one position; but if we so much as stirred the young men would intervene at once : they would rectify our position, as gently as they could, so as not to disturb our rest : they watched over us in relays so that we never for one second escaped their vigilant eyes.

But perhaps it would be better if I talked about their 'attendance' rather than their 'supervision'; they were more like nurses than superiors. By day, when, weary of continually sitting or lying on our mats, we asked to be allowed to get up, they would help us; indeed, at every step we took they would be at our sides supporting us. They would go and collect our food, take news of our progress to our parents, and bring us news of them. Their task was no sinecure; we took their good nature for granted, and at times took advantage of it; but they never grumbled : they looked after us with boundless goodwill.

Our healer was not so indulgent. He doubtlessly gave us the utmost devotion in his attendance upon us; but he was something of a disciplinarian, though not a harsh one; but he did not like us to pull a face when he was cleaning our wound.

'You are not little boys now,' he would tell us. 'Control yourselves.'

And we just had to control ourselves, if we did not want to be called hopeless little snivellers. So twice a day we would keep a stiff upper lip, for our healer used to clean our wound in the morning, then in the evening. He would use water in which certain kinds of bark had been steeping, and as he cleaned the wounds he would pronounce heading incantations. The task of teaching and initiating us also fell to him.

After the first week, which was passed entirely in the solitude of the hut, and whose monotony had been broken by a few visits from my father, we had recovered enough liberty of movement to be able to go for short walks in the bush, escorted by our healer.

As long as we remained in the immediate vicinity of the town, the young men would walk in front. They acted as scouts, so that, should some woman be found walking in our direction, they could warn her in time of our approach, and she could go some other away. Indeed our wounds had properly healed. The rule is enforced simply to avoid any delay in the healing of the wound; I do not think any other explanation need be sought.

The teaching we received in the bush, far from all prying eyes, had nothing very mysterious about it; nothing, I think, that was not fit for ears other than our own. These lessons, the same as had been taught to all those who had gone before us, confined themselves to outlining the sort of conduct befitting a man: to be absolutely straightforward, to cultivate all the virtues that go to make an honest man, to fulfil our duties towards God, towards our parents, our superiors and our neighbour. And we had to tell nothing of what we learned, either to women or to the uninitiated; neither had we to reveal any of the secret rites of circumcision. That is the custom. Women, too, are not allowed to tell anything about the rites of excision.

Should a non-initiate attempt later on to find out what we had been taught, and try to pass himself off as an initiate in order to do so, we were told how to expose him. The simplest, though not the least laborious way, was by using phrases with refrains that had to be whistled in a certain way. There are very many of these refrains; so many that should the impostor, by some extraordinary chance, have learned two or three, he will find himself baffled by the fourth or the tenth. if not by the twentieth.

Always lengthy, always complicated, it is impossible to imitate these refrains unless they have been whistled time and time again, and patiently learnt by heart.

They really require very patient study, and an agile memory, if one is to retain them all, as we finally realised. Whenever our healer thought we were not learning them fast enough – and indeed we were not always very attentive – he would remind us sharply of our duty; he would avail himself of the pompom on our cap, with which he would belabour our backs. That would not hurt very much, you may say; but if the pompom is a large one, bound tightly with cotton and with something hard inside, it can be very painful.

By the third week, I was allowed to see my mother. When one of the younger men came and said my mother was at the door, I leapt to my feet.

'Here, not so fast,' he said, taking me by the hand. 'Wait for me.'

'All right, but hurry.'

Three weeks! Never before had we been separated from each other for so long. When I used to go on holiday to Tindican, I would seldom stay away longer that ten or fifteen days, and that was not to be compared with the length of our present separation.

'Well, are you coming?' I cried.

I was quivering with impatience.

'Listen,' said the young man. 'Listen first of all to what I have to say. You are going to see your mother, you are allowed to see her; but you must stand within the fence when speaking to her; you must not go beyond the fence.'

'I'll stay inside the fence,' I said. 'Just let me go.'

And I tried to shake off his hand.

'We'll go together,' he said.

He had not let go of my hand. We left the hut together. The gate in the fence was open. Several of the young men were sitting on the threshold; they signalled to me not to go beyond it. With a few swift strides I covered the few yards that separated me from the gate, and suddenly I saw my mother. She was standing in the dusty road a few steps away from the fence; she, too, was forbidden to come any closer.

'Mother!' I cried. 'Mother!'

And all at once I felt a lump in my throat. Was it because I could go no closer, because I could not hug my mother? Was it because we had already been separated so long, because we were still to be separated a long time? I do not know. All I know is that I could only say 'Mother!' and that after my joy in seeing her I suddenly felt a strange depression. Ought I to attribute this emotional instability to the transformation that had been worked in me? When I had left my mother, I was still a child. Now . . . But was I really a man now? Was I already a grown man? . . . I *was* a man! Yes, I was a grown man. And now this manhood had already begun to stand between my mother and myself. It kept us infinitely further apart than the few yards that separated us now.

'Mother!' I said again.

But this time I spoke it very low, like a lament, sadly, as if it were a lament for myself.

'Yes, here I am,' said my mother. 'I've come to see you.'

'Yes, you've come to see me.'

And suddenly I passed from sadness to joy. What was I worrying about? My mother was there. She was here in front of me. I only had to go a couple of steps and I would be at her side; I would certainly have done so if there had not been that absurd order forbidding me to go beyond the gate.

'I am glad to see you,' went on my mother.

She smiled. At once I understood why she was smuing. When she came she had been a little uneasy, vaguely uneasy. Even though she had had news of my progress, even though my father himself had taken her news of me, and good news, nevertheless she had remained a little uneasy: how did she know that she was being told the truth? But now that she had been to see for herself, she had been able to judge for herself from how I looked that my convalescence was well under way, and she was really glad.

'I am really very glad,' she said.

Nevertheless, she did not say anything more; this casual reference was enough. One must not speak openly of anyone's return to health, especially ours; that would not be wise; it would be tempting hostile spirits to attack us.

'I brought you some kola nuts,' my mother said.

And she opened the little basket she held in her hand and showed me the nuts. One of the young men, who was sitting by the gate, went and took them and gave them to me.

'Thank you, Mother.'

'Now I must be getting back home,' she said.

'Say good-bye for me to my father, and to everyone.'

'Yes, I shall do so.'

'It won't be long now, Mother.'

'Not very long,' she replied.

Her voice was trembling a little. I went in at once. Our meeting had not lasted two minutes, but that was all we were allowed. And all the time between us there had been that space that could not be crossed. Poor dear little mother! She had not even held me in her arms. Nevertheless, I am sure she walked away with head held high, and with great dignity; she always used to hold herself very straight, and so appeared taller than she really was. I seemed to see her walking along the dusty road, her dress falling in noble folds, her waistband neatly tied, her hair carefully plaited and drawn back on to the nape of her neck. How long those three weeks must have seemed to her !

I walked for a while in the yard before going back into the hut. I felt sad, I was feeling sad again. Had I, in losing my childhood, lost my carefree spirits too? I rejoined my companions, shared my nuts with them; their generally so pleasant bitterness, so refreshing to the palate, was now no more than the purest gall.

My father, of course, came often; he could visit me as often as he liked. But we did not have much to say to one another : those visits, in the midst of my companions, and the young men, had no real intimacy about them.

During the fourth week we were allowed more liberty. Our wounds had for the most part healed or else were making such good progress that there was no danger of set-backs to our convalescence. By the end of the week we had completely recovered. The young men took the framework out of our hats and unpicked our boubous. We were now wearing wide trousers, and we were, of course, very anxious to be seen again in public. We went for a walk in the town, very proud of ourselves, immensely proud of our new attire, and talking at the top of our voices, as if we were not already drawing enough attention to ourselves.

We still remained in a group, and it was again in this single group that we made a round of visits to the various compounds to which we belonged. We were fêted everywhere we went, and we did ample justice always to the banquet that awaited us; now that we were almost well again – several of us were in fact quite well again; I for my part, had completely recovered – we had wonderful appetites.

Whenever an uncircumcised boy came rather too close to our happy band, we would seize him and belabour him playfully with our pompoms. But we were still forbidden all contact with girls, and this was a ban which no one thought of breaking. I caught sight of Fanta, and she waved to me at a discreet distance; I answered her likewise by simply fluttering my eyelids. Was I still in love with her? I did not know. We had been so cut off from the world, we had become so different from what we had been, even though a mere month had elapsed between our childhood and our entry into manhood; we had become so indifferent to all that we had been before, that I no longer knew quite where I was. 'Time,' I thought, 'time will help me to settle down again.' But how? I had no idea.

Finally the time came when the healer considered us completely recovered and handed us over to our parents again. But I was still at school and I could no longer join in the excursions which my companions were going on among the neighbouring towns and villages. Nor could I take part in their labours in our healer's fields, work which they undertook to repay the care he had taken of us. My parents arranged with him for me to be exempted from it.

When I finally got back to my compound, the whole family was waiting for me. My parents held me tightly in their arms, particularly my mother, as if she was waiting secretly to proclaim that I was still her son, that my second birth had done nothing to alter the fact that I was still her son. My father watched us for a moment, then he said to me, almost regretfully:

'From now on, this is your hut, my son.'

The hut stood opposite my mother's.

'Yes,' said my mother, 'you will sleep there now. But as you can see, I am still within earshot.'

I opened the door of the hut; my clothes were laid out on the bed. I went up to it and took them in my hands one by one, then put them carefully back; they

were men's clothes. Yes, the hut was opposite my
mother's, I was still within earshot of her voice, but the
clothes on the bed were men's clothes. I was a man!

'Are you pleased with your new clothes?' asked my
mother.

Pleased? Yes, I was pleased; naturally I was pleased.
At least I think I was pleased. They were fine clothes,
they were . . . I turned towards my mother : she was
smiling sadly at me . . .

Nine

I WAS fifteen when I left home for Conakry, where I
was going to pursue a course of technical studies at the
Ecole Georges-Poiret, now known as the Technical
College.

I was leaving my parents for the second time. The
first time was immediately after I had passed my scholarship examination, when I had acted as interpreter to an
officer who had come to map the land in our district and
in part of the neighbouring Sudan. But on this second
occasion, I was taking much lengthier leave of them.

For a whole week, my mother had been gathering
together provisions for me. Conakry is about 400 miles
from Kouroussa, and to my mother it was an unknown
if not unexplored land, where God alone knew if I would
get enough to eat. And so she collected together couscous, meat, fish, yams, rice and potatoes. The previous
week my mother had already undertaken a tour of the
most celebrated marabouts, consulting them about my
future and making many sacrifices. She had offered up
an ox in memory of her father and had invoked the aid
of her ancestors' spirits, in order that good fortune might

attend me on a voyage which, in her eyes, was rather like departing for a savage land; the fact that Conakry is the capital of Guinea only served to accentuate the strange character of the place where I was going.

On the eve of my departure, all the marabouts and witch-doctors, friends and notables, and, it must be said, whoever cared to cross our threshold, all attended a magnificent feast in our compound. For my mother believed that on this occasion no one should be turned away; on the contrary, representatives of all classes of society had to attend the feast, so that the blessing I was to take with me would be complete. Moreover, this was the reason why the marabouts had requested such large quantities of food. And so each guest, after having eaten his fill, would seize me by the hand and bless me, saying:

'May good fortune favour you! May your studies be fruitful! And may the Lord protect you!'

As for the marabouts, they used much lengthier phrases. They would begin by reciting a few quotations from the Koran, adapting them to the occasion; then, having completed their invocations, they would utter the name of Allah; whereupon they would bless me.

I passed a wretched night. I was very depressed, a little upset, and I woke up several times. Once I seemed to hear groans. I guessed immediately that it was my mother. I got up and went to her hut: my mother was tossing on her bed and quietly lamenting. Perhaps I should have gone to her and tried to console her, but I did not know how she would take it; maybe she would not have liked to think she had been found weeping and wailing; and I withdrew with a heavy heart. Is this what life was going to be like? Were tears a part of everything we did?

My mother woke me at dawn, and I got up at once. I saw that her face was strained, but she was determined to keep control of herself and I said nothing. I pretended that her apparent calm had really convinced me. My luggage was piled up in the hut. Carefully wrapped and in a prominent position was a large bottle.

'What's in the bottle?' I asked.

'Do not break it,' said my mother.

'I'll look after it.'

'Take great care of it. And every morning, before you begin your studies, take a little sip of it.'

'Is it supposed to be good for the brain?'

'It is indeed. It's the best there is: it comes from Kankan.'

I had already drunk some of this liquid: my teacher had made me drink some when I was sitting my scholarship examinations. It is a magic potion that possesses many qualities: it is particularly good for developing the brain. It is a curious mixture: our marabouts have small boards on which they write prayers taken from the Koran. When they have written down the text, they erase it by washing the board: the washing water is carefully collected, and, with the addition of honey, forms the main part of the elixir. If it was bought in the town of Kankan, which is a strongly Mohammedan town, and the holiest of our native places; and bought, moreover, at a very high price, it must be a particularly potent beverage. My father, for his part, had given me the evening before a he-goat's horn containing talismans; I was to wear this horn all the time, as a protection against evil spirits.

'Run and say your good-byes now,' said my mother.

I had to go and say farewell to the elders of our compound and of the neighbouring compounds. I went with a heavy heart. I had known these men and women since my tenderest years, I had always known them, I had watched them living in this very place, and watched them disappear from it too: my father's mother had disappeared. And would I ever see again these people to whom I was now saying farewell? Overcome by doubts, I felt suddenly as if I was taking leave of the past itself. And indeed, was not that just what I was doing? Was I not leaving behind me here a part of my life?

When I came back to my mother and saw her standing in tears beside my luggage, I, too, began to weep. I implored her not to accompany me to the station, for it seemed to me that if she did I should never be able to tear myself away from her arms. She nodded her consent. We embraced for the last time and I almost ran out of the hut. My sisters and brothers and the apprentices carried my luggage.

My father quickly caught up with me and took my hand, as he used to when I was a little boy. I slowed down : I felt weak, and cried as if my heart was broken.

'Father,' I said.

'I am listening,' he replied.

'Am I really going away?'

'What else could you do? You know quite well that you have to go.'

'Yes,' I said.

And I began to cry again.

'Come, come, my little one! You're a big boy now, aren't you?'

But his very presence, his very kindness – and even more, the fact that he was holding my hand – took away the last vestiges of courage. He understood.

'I shall not go any farther,' he said. 'We shall say good-bye to each other here : it would not do if we burst into tears at the station, in front of your friends. And I do not want to leave your mother alone just now. Your mother is very upset. I am too! We are all terribly upset. But we must be brave. Be brave, my son. My brothers will look after you. But work hard. Work as

you used to work here. We have made many sacrifices
for you : they must not be for nothing. Do you hear
me ?'

'Yes,' I said.

He remained silent for a moment, then went on :

'You see, I had no father to look after me, as you
had. At least, not for very long : when I was twelve
years old I became an orphan; and I had to make my
own way in life. It was not easy. The uncles in whose
care I was left treated me more like a slave than a
nephew. Not that I was a burden to them for very long :
they hired me out to the Syrians almost at once. I was
simply a domestic drudge, and I had to hand over everything I earned to my uncles. But even so it did not
diminish their cruelty and greed. I always had to keep
my own counsel and work hard to make a name for
myself. You . . . But I have said enough. Seize your
opportunity. And make me proud of you. I ask no more
of you. Will you do it ?'

'I will, Father.'

'Good ! Good . . . Well, be brave, son. Good-bye.'

'Father !'

He held me close; he had never held me so close
before.

'Good-bye, little one, good-bye.'

Abruptly he let me go and walked away very fast —
perhaps he did not want to let me see his tears. I went
on along the road to the station. My eldest sister, my
brothers, Sidafa and the younger apprentices went with
me carrying my luggage. As we walked along, we were
joined by friends; Fanta joined us too. And it was rather
as if I was on my way to school again : all my companions were there, but there had never been so many
before. Was I not, indeed, on my way to school?

'Fanta,' I said, 'we are on the way to school.'

But the only answer she gave me was a faint smile, and

that was the only answer my words received. I was indeed on the way to school, but I was alone; I was already alone . . . There had never been so many of us, but never had I felt so alone. Although it was perhaps worst for me, we all shared the pain of parting. We spoke little. And soon we were standing on the railway platform, waiting for the train, but we hardly said one word to each other.

Several praise-singers had come to celebrate my departure. I had no sooner reached the station than they began to beset me with their flatteries. 'Already thou art as wise as the White Man,' they sang. 'Thou art verily as wise as the White Man. In Conakry, thou shalt take thy place even among the most illustrious.' Such excessive praises had the effect of subduing, rather than of inflaming my vanity. What did I know, after all? I was still very far from 'wise'. The friends who were with me were as wise as I was! I should have liked to ask the praise-singers to stop, or at least to moderate their flattery; but that would have been contrary to custom, so I remained silent. Perhaps their flatteries were after all not altogether useless : they made me determined to take my work seriously. True, I had always done so; but now I felt myself obliged to bring to pass, one day, everything that the praise-singers were chanting, if, on my return, I did not wish to look a fool.

These flatteries had an additional effect : they kept me from thinking of the sadness I felt. They had made me smile – before they began to embarrass me – but, even though my companions, too, had felt how ridiculous they were – it was natural they they should feel how ridiculous they were – they allowed nothing of this to appear on their faces; perhaps we are so accustomed to the hyperboles of our praise-singers that we no longer take very much notice of them. But what about Fanta? No, Fanta must have taken all those flatteries for the

truth. Fanta . . . Fanta never thought of smiling: her
eyes were filled with tears. Dear Fanta! . . . Despairingly,
I cast a glance at my sister. She must surely know how
I felt; she always felt as I did. But I saw she was simply
looking after my luggage; she had already told me
several times to keep my eye on it, and when our eyes
met she told me again.

'Don't worry,' I said. 'I'll keep an eye on it.'

'Do you remember how many cases there are?'

'Of course.'

'Good. Now don't lose any. Remember you are
staying the first night at Mamou. The train stops for the
night at Mamou.'

'You don't have to explain everything to me. I'm
not a child.'

'No, but you don't know what sort of people they'll
be down there. Keep your luggage beside you, and count
it from time to time. You understand? Keep your eye
on it.'

'Yes,' I said.

'And be careful with strangers. D'you hear me?'

'I hear you.'

But already I had stopped listening to her and to the
songs of the praise-singers. My sadness suddenly returned. My little brothers had slipped their little hands
into mine, and I kept thinking how warm and soft their
hands were; I kept thinking, too, that the train would
soon be here, and that I should have to let go their
hands and leave their tender warmth, leave their gentle-
ness; and I began to feel afraid of seeing the train appear,
I began to hope it would be late. Sometimes it was
late; perhaps it would be late today. I looked at the
clock. It *was* late! . . . But suddenly it appeared and I
had to let go of their hands and leave their gentle pres-
sure behind, as if it was the whole of my life.

They passed my luggage to me through the window,

and I put it all over the seats. My sister gave me some last words of advice that were as useless as all the others she had given me: and everyone had something nice to say to me, Fanta and Sidafa especially. But in all that waving of hands and scarves that accompanied the train's departure, I only really saw my brothers, who ran the length of the platform, the length of the train, shouting good-bye. At the point where the platform ended, my sister and Fanta joined them, waving their head-scarves. And then, suddenly, they disappeared from sight, long before the first bend of the track, for a sudden mist enveloped them, and tears blinded my eyes. ... For a long time I lay prostrate in a corner of my compartment, with my luggage strewn all round me, and with the final sight ever before my eyes: my young brothers, my sister, Fanta ...

Towards midday, the train reached Dabola. I had sorted out my luggage at last and counted it; I was beginning to take a little interest once more in things and people. I heard Peuhl spoken: Dabola is on the borders of the Peuhl country. The great plain on which I had lived until now, that plain which was so rich, so poor also, so hard-fisted sometimes, with its sun-scorched earth, but nonetheless a familiar, friendly face, was giving place to the foothills of the Fouta-Djalon.

The train started again, going in the direction of Mamou. Soon the lofty cliffs of the mountains appeared. They were barring the horizon, and the train was going to conquer them. But it was a very slow conquest, almost a hopeless one; so slow and so hopeless that sometimes the train proceeded at barely more than a walking pace. This country, new to me, too new to me, too agitated, disconcerted rather than enchanted me; its beauty escaped me.

I arrived at Mamou a little before nightfall. As the train does not go on from this town until the next day,

the passengers pass the night in a hotel or with friends.
A former apprentice of my father's, who had been told
I was passing through the town, had offered me hos-
pitality for the night. This apprentice had written in
the most affectionate terms; actually – but perhaps he
had forgotten the difference in climate – he lodged me
in a dark hut on top of a hill, where I had ample leisure
– more than I wanted – to experience the chill nights
and the keen air of the Fouta-Djalon. Mountains certainly did not agree with me!

The next day, I continued my train journey. But a
complete change had taken place in me. Was I getting
used to it already? I do not know; but my feelings
about mountains were suddenly modified, so much so
that, from Mamou to Kindia, I did not leave the window
for a moment. I was watching, with enchantment now,
a succession of peaks and precipices, torrents and cas-
cades of water, wooded slopes and deep valleys. Water
sprang and flowed everywhere, and gave a kind of animation to everything. It was a wonderful spectacle;
a little terrifying, too, whenever the train seemed to go
too close to the edge of precipices. And because the air
was of an extraordinary purity, everything could be seen
in the minutest detail. It was a happy land, or at least
it seemed happy. There were innumerable flocks of
grazing sheep, and the shepherds would wave to us as
we passed.

When we stopped at Kindia, I no longer heard Peuhl
spoken; they were speaking Soussou, which is the dialect
spoken in Conakry. I listened for a while; but I understood very little of what was said.

Now we were descending towards the coast and towards Conakry. The train went on and on; just as it
had seemed to puff painfully up the mountains, now
it seemed to be rolling joyfully down. But the landscape
was no longer like what it had been between Mamou

and Kindia : it was no longer quite so picturesque. Here
was a less animated territory, less wild and already more
domesticated, in which vast symmetrical expanses of
banana-trees or palm-trees followed each other mono-
tonously. The heat was also overpowering, and became
even more so as we approached the lower ground of the
coast, while the humidity increased; naturally, the air
was not so clear.

As night was falling, the peninsula of Conakry came
in sight, brightly illuminated. I caught sight of it from
far off, like a huge shining flower laid on the sea; it was
joined to the mainland by its stalk. The water all round
it was shining softly, shining like the heavens; but the
sky does not possess that quivering animation. Almost
at once, the flower began to expand, and the water
receded : for a few moments more, it lay on each side
of the stalk, then it disappeared. We were now getting
rapidly nearer. When we had entered the lights themselves of the peninsula, the heart of the flower, the train
came to a stop.

A tall, imposing man came up to me. I had never
seen him before – or rather, I had seen him, but I was
too young to remember – but by the way he looked at
me I guessed that he was my father's brother.

'Are you my father's brother Mamadou?' I asked.

'Yes,' he replied, 'and you must be my nephew
Laye. I recognised you at once : you are the living
image of your mother. Really, I could not have failed
to recognise you. Tell me, how is your mother? And
how is your father? . . . But come along, we shall have
leisure to speak of all those things later. The essential
thing at the moment is for you to have something to
eat and a good night's rest. So come with me, and you
will find your dinner ready and your room in order.'

That night was the first I had passed in a European-
style house. Was it the unfamiliarity, or the humid heat

of the town, or the fatigue of two days in the train that made me sleep badly? It was nevertheless a very comfortable house, and the room I was sleeping in was big enough, the bed very soft, softer than any bed I had hitherto slept on; moreover, I had been very warmly welcomed, as if I had been a son of the house. It was no good: I missed Kouroussa, I missed my little hut. All my thoughts were turned to Kouroussa; and I felt very lonely, despite the affectionate welcome I had been given.

'Well,' said my uncle, when I appeared before him in the morning, 'have you slept well?'

'Yes,' I said.

'No,' he said, 'I don't think you have slept very well. Perhaps the change was too sudden. But you will soon get used to it here. You'll sleep a great deal better tonight. You will, won't you?'

'I think so.'

'Good. And what are you thinking of doing today?'

'I don't know. Should I not pay a visit to the school?'

'We shall do that tomorrow; we shall go together. Today you will have a look round the town. Take advantage of this last day of your holidays! Don't you agree with me?'

'Yes, Uncle.'

I went to have a look round the town. It was very different from Kouroussa. The avenues here were as straight as rulers and crossed each other at right angles. They were lined with mango-trees, that also stood here and there in shady groups: their thick shade was always welcome, for the heat was overpowering. Not that it was much worse than at Kouroussa – perhaps it was even less intense – but it was saturated with moisture to an incredible extent. The houses were all embowered in flower and foliage; many seemed to be as it were lost in all the vegetation, drowned in a frantic proliferation of greenery. And then, I saw the sea . . .

I saw it all of a sudden at the end of an avenue. I stood a long time looking at its vastness, watching the waves that kept rolling in after one another and finally were broken against the red rocks of the shore. Far off there appeared, in spite of the mist that hung around them, some very green-looking islands. It seemed to me the most astonishing spectacle I had ever seen; from the train, at night, I had only glimpsed what it was like; I had formed no real idea of the vastness of the ocean, and even less of its movement, of the kind of irresistible fascination which comes from its inexhaustibly endless movement. Now that the whole spectacle lay before me, it was only with difficulty that I dragged myself away from it.

My uncle lived in the house with his two wives, my aunts Awa and N'Gady, and a younger brother, my Uncle Sékou. My aunts, like my uncles, had each their own room, which they occupied with their own children.

From the very first, my aunts Awa and N'Gady were very fond of me, so much so that soon they made no distinction between their children and myself. As for the children, very much younger than me, they were not told that I was their cousin; they believed I was their elder brother and forthwith treated me as such; never a day passed without their running to me and climbing on my knees. Later, when I had formed the habit of spending all my holidays at my uncle's, they even would come running to meet me. No sooner had they heard or seen me than they would come racing up; and if it happened that they were absorbed by a game and did not come running at once, my aunts would scold them : 'What's this?' they would cry, 'it's a whole week since you saw your big brother, and you don't run to bid him good-day?' Yes, my two aunts really put themselves out to take my mother's place; and they went on doing so all the time I was with them.

My Uncle Mamadou was a little younger than my father; he was tall and strong, always very correctly dressed, calm and dignified; he was a man who made himself felt at once. Like my father, he was born in Kouroussa, but had left it at an early age; he had gone to school there; then, as I was doing now, he had come to Conakry to continue his studies and had completed them at the *Ecole Normale de Gorée*. I believe he was not teaching long, for the world of business had claimed him very soon. When I arrived at Conakry he was managing director in a French establishment. I gradually got to know him better. And the more I got to know him, the more I loved and respected him.

He was a Mohammedan, as we all are, I may add; but in really a much better way than is generally the case. His interpretation of the Koran was scrupulously correct. He did not smoke, he did not drink; he was absolutely honest. He only wore European clothes when he went to work; as soon as he came back home, he would undress and put on a boubou, which had to be immaculate, and say his prayers. On leaving the Ecole Normale, he had taken up the study of Arabic; he had learned it thoroughly, though without any help, using bilingual books and a dictionary; now he could speak it as well as French, though without any desire to show off, for it was solely a deeper knowledge of religion that had persuaded him to learn the language of the Prophet; he had been inspired by a great longing to read the Koran in the original. The Koran guided him in everything he did. I never saw my uncle in a temper, and I never saw him enter into a dispute with his wives; he was always calm, master of himself, and infinitely patient. He was held in great esteem in Conakry, and

I merely had to say who my uncle was for some of that prestige to be accorded to me also. I looked upon him as a saint.

My Uncle Sékou, the youngest of my father's brothers, had none of this intransigence; in one way, he was much closer to me : his youth seemed to make him closer to me. There was in him an exuberance of spirit which delighted me, and which manifested itself in a great flow of words. He had only to begin to speak and he became inexhaustible. I loved to listen to him – everyone loved to listen to him – because he never said anything meaningless, and he always said it with marvellous eloquence. I will add that his exuberance had very serious qualities, and that these qualities were sensibly the same as those possessed by my Uncle Mamadou. At the period when I knew him he was still unmarried – only affianced – which was an additional reason for bringing us closer together. He was employed by the Conakry-Niger railway. To me, he, too, was always without fault; and because our ages were not so far apart, he was more of a brother to me than an uncle.

After the last day of the holidays, my Uncle Mamadou took me to my new school.

'Work hard now,' he said, 'and the Lord will keep you. You can give me your first impressions on Sunday.'

In the courtyard, where I was given my first instructions, and in the dormitory where I went to arrange my clothes, I found pupils who like myself had come from Upper Guinea; we became acquainted, and I did not feel so lonely. A little later, we went into our classrooms. We were all of us, new and old pupils, assembled in the same vast room. I was prepared to take everything in with both ears, hoping to profit from some part of the teaching given to the older boys, at the same time paying attention to whatever the younger ones were taught; but almost at once I saw that not much distinction was made between the elder and the younger boys. It seemed rather as if we were getting ready to learn the lessons that had twice or even three times already been crammed into the older boys since their first year. 'Well, we'll see,' I said to myself. But nevertheless I was perturbed : such a proceeding did not seem to me to augur well.

To start with, a very simple text was dictated to us. When the teacher marked the copies, I was surprised that they could contain so many faults. It was, as I have said, a very simple text, without pitfalls, and one which any of my companions in Kouroussa would have had no difficulty with. Afterwards we were given a problem to solve, and only two of us found the right answer. I was stunned : was this the school where I was to rise to the highest grade? It seemed to me rather as if I was going back several years, that I was still sitting in one of the infants' classes at Kouroussa. And that is exactly how it was : the whole week went by without my having learnt a thing. On the Sunday, I complained bitterly to my uncle :

'But I've learnt nothing, Uncle! I already know by heart all the things they taught us. Is it really worth while going to this school? I might as well go back to Kouroussa at once !'

'No,' said my uncle, 'wait a little.'

'There's nothing to wait for. I could see at once that there was nothing worth waiting for.'

'Come, do not be so impatient. Are you always as impatient as this? The school where you are now is perhaps of too low a grade in general subjects, but it can give you practical training which you will find nowhere else. Haven't you been in the workshops?'

I showed him my hands : they were covered with scratches and the tips of my fingers burned.

'But I do not want to be a workman,' I said.

'Why not?'

'I do not want to be despised.'

In the general view, there was a tremendous difference between the pupils at our school and those at the Camille-Guy college. We were looked upon simply as future working men; certainly we would never be skilled men, but we might at the very most become foremen; unlike the pupils at the Camille-Guy, we would never be able to enter the colleges in Dakar.

'Listen to me carefully,' said my uncle. 'All the pupils who come from Kouroussa hold the Technical School in scorn, they all dream of a position as a clerk. Is that the sort of career you want? Clerks are ten a penny. If you really want that sort of career, change your school. But remember this: if I were twenty years younger, if I still had my schooling to do, I would not go to the *Ecole Normale*; no, I would learn a good trade in a technical school. A good trade would have taken me a lot further.'

'But I might as well never have left my father's forge,' I said.

'Maybe not. But, tell me, have you never had any ambition to do better than that?'

Now I *was* ambitious. But I would never realise my ambitions by becoming a manual worker; I had no more respect than most people for such workers.

'But who is speaking of manual work?' said my uncle. 'A technician is not necessarily a manual worker, and in any case, there are other things in his line of work: he is a man who has others under him and who can turn his hand to anything should the need arise. Now men who are in charge of businesses do not always know how to turn their hand to anything, and that is where you will score. Believe me, stay where you are. And I'm going to tell you something you don't know: your school is about to be reorganised. You will shortly

see great changes there, and the general standard of
education will not be inferior to that at the Camille-Guy
college.'

Did my uncle's arguments finally convince me? Not
altogether perhaps. But my Uncle Sékou and even my
aunts added their advice to his, and so I stayed at the
technical school.

For four days out of the six, I used to work in the
workshops, filing bits of iron or planing boards under
the direction of a monitor. It was apparently easy and
not uninteresting work; but it was not as easy as it
appeared at first sight, because first of all the lack of
practice, and secondly the long hours we spent standing
in front of the benches, all helped to make it very boring.
I don't know how it was – was it through having to
stand so much? was it some kind of inflammation set
up by wooden and metal splinters? – my feet began to
swell and an ulcer developed on them. I believe that at
Kouroussa such a thing would not have been malignant;
I think it would not even have happened; but here, in
this burning, moisture-laden heat, in this climate that
my body had not had time to adapt itself to, the ulcer
rapidly gained ground. I was sent to hospital.

My spirits suddenly dropped. The more than spartan
fare which was given us in this otherwise magnificent
hospital was not really intended to raise the spirits. But
as soon as my aunts learnt what had happened to me,
they brought my meals each day; my uncles visited me
too, and kept me company. Without them, I should
have been really miserable, really lonely, in that city
whose ways were foreign to me, whose climate was
hostile, and whose dialect I could barely follow. All
around me, only Soussou was spoken; and I am a
Malinke; apart from French, the only language I speak
is Malinke.

Then I began to think it was silly to lie there twiddling

E

my thumbs, breathing sticky air, sweating night and day: I began to think it was even sillier not to be at school, to have to swelter in such a suffocating atmosphere, and in such useless immobility. What was I doing, if not wasting my time? The ulcer was not getting any better. It was not getting any worse, but it was not getting any better either: it just stayed where it was.

The school year passed slowly, very slowly, indeed it seemed endless to me, as endless as the interminable rains that beat for days, sometimes weeks, on the corrugated iron roofs; as endless as my interminable sickness. Then, by a strange coincidence which I cannot explain, the ending of the scholastic year coincided with my return to health. But it was not before time: I was choking, bubbling over with impatience . . . I set off for Kouroussa again, as if for a promised land.

Ten

WHEN, in October, after the holidays, I returned to Conakry, the reorganisation which my uncle had talked about was in full swing: the school had changed completely. New class-rooms had been made, a new head had been appointed, and teachers had come from France. I was soon receiving an irreproachable technical education and teaching in general subjects which was sufficiently advanced. I no longer envied the pupils of the Camille-Guy; I was receiving the same education as they received, and in addition a technical and practical training which they did not have. The older pupils had gone: the Conakry-Niger railway had engaged them all. And so everything began again, for the first-year pupils onwards. My Uncle Mamadou had not been mistaken and he had not deceived me. I was learning frenziedly everything that came my way, and each term my name was on the list of honour. My uncle was over-joyed.

It was during that year, that first year, since the pre-ceding one no longer counted, that I became friendly with Marie.

Whenever I think about our friendship, and I often think about it, dream about it – I am always dreaming about it – it seems to me that there was nothing, in all those years, to surpass it! nothing in all those years of exile, that meant more to me. And it was not because I was lacking in affection; my aunts, and my uncles too, gave me all their affection; but I was at the age when the heart cannot rest until it has found some object to cherish, when it can brook no shackles but its own, more powerful and more demanding than any others. But are we not always at this age, are we not always consumed by longing? Is our heart ever at rest?

Marie was a pupil at the girls' High School. Her father, before studying medicine and setting up a prac-tice in Bela, had been the schoolboy companion of my Uncle Mamadou, and they were still great friends, so that Marie used to spend all her Sundays in my uncle's house, finding there, as I did, the warmth of a family hearth. She was a half-caste, with a very light skin, almost white in fact, and very beautiful, surely the most beautiful girl of all the girls in the girls' High School. To me, she seemed as beautiful as a fairy. She was sweet and charming, and with a most wonderfully even temper. And she had exceptionally long hair : her tresses hung down to her waist.

On Sundays, she would arrive early at my uncle's : generally much earlier than I did, for I used to dawdle in the streets. As soon as she arrived, she would make a round of the house, greeting everyone; after which she would usually sit with my Aunt Awa: she would put down her satchel, take off her European clothes, put on the Guinean tunic, which allowed greater freedom of movement, and then she would help my aunt with her housework. My aunts liked her very much, and treated her as they did their own, but often teased her about me.

'Well, Marie,' they would say, 'what have you done with your husband?'

'I haven't got a husband yet,' Marie would say.

'Really?' my Aunt N'Gady would say. 'I thought that our nephew was your husband.'

'But I'm not old enough,' Marie would say.

'And when will you be old enough?' Aunt N'Gady would go on.

But Marie would only smile and say nothing to that.

'A smile is not an answer,' my Aunt Awa would say. 'Can't you give us a straightforward answer?'

'I won't tell you, Aunt Awa!'

'That's just what I'm complaining about! When I was your age, I did not have so many secrets.'

'Have I secrets, Auntie? Tell me about when you were a girl like me: you must have had the whole canton running after you, you're so pretty.'

'Did you ever see such a rogue?' my aunt would cry. 'I talk to her about herself, and she talks about me. And not content with that, she talks about my so-called successes . . . Are all the girls at the High School as cunning as you?'

My aunts had very soon noticed our friendship, and they gave it their approval; not only that, they encouraged it. They loved us both equally well; and they would have liked us, despite our youth, to become engaged. But that was more than our timidity would allow.

When I used to arrive home from school, I, too, used

to make a tour of the house, stopping for a moment in each person's room to exchange a few words, and often staying much longer with my Uncle Mamadou, who liked to know every detail of what I had learned and to criticise what I had done. So as soon as I entered Aunt Awa's apartment, she would invariably greet me with the words:

'Look, you've kept Mme Camara Number Three waiting again!'

Mme Camara Number Three was the name she gave to Marie; Aunt Awa was Mme Camara Nmber One, and Aunt N'Gady was Number Two. I used to take the joke with good grace and then bow to Marie.

'Good-day, Mme Camara Number Three,' I would say.

'Good-day, Laye,' she would reply.

And we would shake hands. But Aunt Awa would think us undemonstrative, and she would sigh:

'What slowcoaches you are!' she would say. 'My word, I've never seen two such slowcoaches.'

I would steal away without replying: I did not have Marie's gift for repartee, and Aunt Awa would soon have cornered me. I would begin my round of visits again, with my little cousins at my heels or hanging on to my clothes, the smallest ones in my arms or perched on my shoulders. In the end I would sit down just wherever I felt like it; most often in the garden, for the swarm of children around me would by then be particularly noisy, and I would play with them while waiting for my dinner to be brought to me.

For I always arrived with an empty stomach, terribly empty; this was first of all because I had a naturally good appetite, and secondly because I would not have eaten anything since getting up: on a day off, it would have been a sin to touch the mess we were served up at school; so I would never touch it, considering it quite enough to have to eat it on the other six days of the week. My aunts who, on that day, would cook something very special, would have liked me to take my meals with Marie; but how could I? No, I could not allow it, and I do not think Marie would have liked it either: we would both certainly have felt shy about eating at the same table. We were so very shy, and this shyness was incomprehensible and almost offensive to my aunts: but Marie and I never even discussed it: such was our respect for conventions. We would never think of meeting again until after the meal was over.

Then we nearly always would go to my Uncle Sékou's apartment. His was the quietest part of the house; not that my Uncle Sékou was sparing in his speech – as I have said, he was a prodigious orator – but, being single, he was often out, and we were left alone!

My uncle would leave his gramophone and records for us, and Marie and I would dance. Of course we would dance very circumspectly: it is not customary, in our land, to dance in one another's arms: we dance facing each other, but without touching; at the very most we hold hands, but this was not usual. Need I say that, in our shyness, we desired nothing better? But would we have danced together if it had been customary to dance in one another's arms? I hardly know what we would have done. I think we would have abstained, although, like all Africans, we have dancing in our blood.

But we did not only dance. Marie would take her exercise-books out of her satchel and ask me to help her. It was my opportunity – the best I had, I think, to display my talents; and I would never fail to explain everything, I never missed a single detail.

'You see,' I would say, 'you find first of all the quotient of . . . Marie! Are you listening to me?'

'I'm listening to you.'

'Well, be sure to remember that first you must find out...'

But Marie did not attend very well; perhaps not at all; all she wanted was to see the answer written at the bottom of a problem which, without my help, she would never have solved: the rest did not interest her: the details, the reasons, the methods, the pedantic tone of voice which I probably used, all these were lost on her; and she would sit staring into space. What could she be dreaming about? I could not tell. Perhaps I should say, at that time I did not know. Nowadays, if I think about it, I wonder if it was not our friendship she was dreaming about; perhaps not. Perhaps. But I can see that some explanation is needed here.

Marie loved me, and I loved her, but we never gave the sweet, the awful name 'love' to what we felt. And maybe it was not exactly love, though there was something of that in it. What was it? What could it be? It was certainly something big, something noble: a marvellous tenderness, and an immense happiness. I mean unalloyed happiness, a pure happiness, a happiness still untroubled by desire. But maybe that is what love really is. Certainly it was a child-like passion; and we were still children! Officially I had become a man: I had been initiated. But was that enough? Is it enough just to act like a man? It is years alone that makes a man, and I was still not old enough.

Did Marie hold a different view of our friendship? I do not think so. Was she more worldly-wise than I was? Girls often are; but I do not think Marie was any more than I; and her very modesty – our common modesty – would incline me to think the contrary, although all round her there was a constant unleashing of passions which she must have known something about. But did she really know anything about them? I do not know. I do not know whether her attitude was an unconscious or a purely instinctive one; but I know, I remember that Marie seemed quite blind to everything that went on.

For I was not the only one in love with Marie, though I was perhaps the only one to love her with such innocence. In fact, all my friends were in love with Marie. When, tired of listening to records, tired of dancing, and our lessons finished, we used to go out, I would ride with Marie on the cross-bar of my bicycle, and the young men of Conakry, particularly my school-friends and the college boys from the Camille-Guy, would watch us go by with envious glances. They would all have liked to go walking with Marie; but Marie used to ignore them : she only had eyes for me.

It is not pride or vanity that makes me remember this, though at the time I was very proud of my good fortune. No, I remember our love with feelings of piercing sweetness, I think and dream about it, dream about it with feelings of inexplicable melancholy, because it seems to me now that I lived then one last and fragile moment of my youth, a moment in which all my young body seemed to take fire. It is a moment I shall never recapture, and which now has only the bitter-sweet charm of something vanished for ever.

I would generally ride my bicycle in the direction of the corniche. There, we would dismount, sit down and watch the sea. When, on my arrival in Conakry, I had made a tour of the place and suddenly discovered the sea, I had fallen in love with it at once. That vast plain. . . . Yes, maybe that vast plain of water reminded me of another plain : the great plain of Upper Guinea where I had grown up . . . I do not know. But even supposing that the attraction the sea had for me might have diminished since my first glimpse of it, I would still have come to watch it from the corniche; for Marie, too, liked nothing as much as to come and sit here and watch the sea, just to sit and watch it until she could watch it no more.

The sea is very beautiful, seen from the corniche, and shot with brilliant colours: it is opaque at the edges, mingling the blue of the sky with the shining green of the coco and palm trees on the shore, and fringed with foam – a rainbow fringe, farther out, it has a pearly lustre. The islands of coco trees which can be seen in the distance floating in a slightly misted, vaporous radiance, have such fresh, delicate shades that you feel your heart overflowing with happiness at the sight. And moreover, there is wafted from the open sea a breeze which, though slight, nevertheless moderates a little the oven-like heat of the town.

'You can breathe!' I would say. 'Here you can breathe!'

'Yes,' Marie would say.

'Do you see those little islands over there? I'll bet you could breathe there even more freely than on the corniche.'

'I'm sure you could,' Marie would answer.

'Wouldn't you like to go there?'

'Where?' she would say, 'to the islands? But it's sea all round.'

'Yes of course it's sea all round.'

'But nobody ever goes to those islands. They are desert islands.'

'The fishermen go there. We could take a boat, and within half an hour we would be there.'

'Take a boat?' Marie would say.

And out of the corner of her eye she would seem to be measuring the violence of the waves which were dashing against the red rocks on the shore.

'I wouldn't like to go in a boat,' she would say. 'Can't you see how rough the sea is?'

Yes, the sea was rough; it was thundering violently

against the shore. A boat was a very fragile thing to venture out in against such strength. The fishermen were not afraid of it, but we were not fisherman. We would have had to know, as they do, the places where the sea is calmer, and how to tame its wildness; but I knew nothing of the sea. I used to venture out on the Niger, of course, but the sea's power was different. The Niger flows with a tranquil strength; it *is* tranquil; it would rouse itself a little only in times of flood. Whereas the sea was never tranquil; it was never at rest, but constantly rising with rebellious force.

'We could ask some of the fishermen to take us there,' I would say.

'Why?' Marie would ask. 'You don't need them in order to get there, you don't even need a boat: all you need is the sight of your two eyes. If you watch the islands for a long time, if you can stare at them without blinking, or gaze at one of them so long that it begins to tremble, it's almost as good as having landed on it: you *are* on the island.'

'Do you really think so?'

'Listen . . . you can even hear the breeze blowing through the coco trees; you can hear the rustling of the coco trees.'

But the sound really came from over our heads; it was in the tops of the coco trees planted along the edge of the coast that the breeze was blowing, it was merely the palm fronds on our own coco trees that were rustling. And the enchantment suddenly faded. We both burst out laughing.

What else did we talk about? About school, of course. We would tell each other the latest gossip about our respective schools; maybe, too, we would talk about the past, perhaps I would talk about Kouroussa and about my holidays at Tindican. What else? I don't know, I really don't know. Doubtless we concealed nothing from one another, except our friendship, except our hearts; our hearts were like the green isles that we used to watch trembling on the horizon in misty radiance. We could travel there in our thoughts, but we could not actually approach them. Our friendship was an inward thing, inhabiting the very depths of our being. It had to remain unspoken; one word, a single word would perhaps have frightened it away; one word, too, could have altered it irrevocably. And we did not expect it to alter; we liked it as it was. It might seem from this we were everything, and nothing, to one another : but we were always everything, and never nothing, to one another : no one had ever been closer to my heart than Marie, no one had ever dwelt within my heart like Marie.

By now, night would be falling, and we would go home. 'Is the day over already?' I would think as I pedalled along. Yes, already this precious Sunday was nearly spent! During the week, time seemed to stand still; on Sundays it raced along without stopping from morning until nightfall; it raced along just as rapidly on rainy Sundays, too, when we would remain shut up in the house, as on fine Sundays. And the dreadful sheets of Conakry rain, so wearisome, so interminable when they hung outside the school-room windows, became blue skies whenever I was with Marie . . .

At the end of the third year I sat the examination for my proficiency certificate. We were warned that a minimum of sixty per cent was required in our marks for technical and classical subjects, and that the engineers living in Conakry would be our examiners. Then the school gave a list of the forty candidates who appeared to have the greatest aptitude. Fortunately I was one of them.

I was absolutely determined to pass my examination. I had studied hard for three years; I had never forgotten the promise I had made to my father, nor yet the one I had made to myself; I had always been among the top three, and I had some hopes that things would not go very differently in the examination. Nevertheless, I wrote to ask my mother to go and see the marabouts and obtain their help. Should I infer from this that I was particularly superstitious at this time? I do not think so. I simply believed that nothing could be óbtained without the help of God, and that if the will of God is something preordained, nevertheless our actions, though just as unforeseen, have their influence on that will. And I felt that the marabouts would be the natural inter-mediaries for me.

My aunts, too, offered up sacrifices, and presented kola nuts to the various persons indicated to them by the marabouts they consulted. I could see they were very anxious about my fate; I believed they were no less so than my mother.

Marie was even more so, if that is possible. She did not attach much importance to her own studies, but I really do not know to what extremities she might have been driven if she had not seen my name among the list of successful candidates in the official newspaper of French Guinea. I learned from my aunts that she, too, had been to see the marabouts; and I really think that touched me more than anything else.

Finally, the day of the examination came. It lasted three days; three days of agony. But we must assume that the marabouts had given me all the help they could. I was placed first out of the seven candidates who passed.

Eleven

EACH TIME I went back home to spend my holidays at Kouroussa, I would find my hut newly decorated with white clay; my mother would be all impatient to show me the improvements which she had made in it from year to year.

At first, my hut was just a hut like any other. And then, gradually, it had begun to take on a more and more Europeanised appearance. I say 'had begun to' for the resemblance always remained partial, though I was very conscious of it; not merely because of the additional comfort it offered, but because it was the living proof, the tangible proof, of the great love my mother felt for me. Yes, I used to pass most of the year at Conakry, but I was still her favourite son: I could see that easily. And I did not need to see it even: I knew it. But in the appearance of my hut I could see it as well as feel it.

'Well, what do you think of it?' my mother would say.

'It's wonderful,' I would reply.

And I would give her a great hug: that was all the thanks my mother expected. But it was indeed 'wonderful' and I did not suspect how much ingenuity had gone into it, how much trouble my mother had taken in order to create – from the simplest materials – those modest equivalents of European mechanical appliances.

The main article of furniture, the one which immediately caught the eye, was the divan bed. At first, it had been just like the one in her own hut, a bed like any other bed in our country, a bed made of clay bricks.

Then the central bricks had been removed, leaving only two supports, one at the foot and one at the head; and planks had taken the place of the bricks. On this improvised bedstead – crude but not uncomfortable – my mother finally placed a mattress stuffed with rice straw. Thus it became a comfortable and fairly spacious bed, big enough for three or even four.

But it was hardly spacious enough to accommodate all the friends, the innumerable friends, both boys and girls, who would come and visit me on certain evenings. I cannot remember just how, piled all together on the bed, we managed to find room to strum a guitar, nor yet how my friends got enough air for singing.

I do not know whether my mother cared very much for these meetings, but she put up with them, comforting herself probably with the thought that at least I was in my own compound, not hanging around Lord knows where. As for my father, he thought it was quite in order. As I scarcely saw him during the day, busy as I was in visiting this or that friend's house (if I had not gone off on some more extensive trip), he would come and knock on my door. I would cry 'Come in!' and he would enter, saying good evening to everyone, and would ask me how I had spent my day. After a few more words, he would go away. He understood that, although his presence was welcome – and it really was – it was at the same time very intimidating to such a youthful and lively gathering as ours.

My mother's attitude was completely different. Her hut was close to mine, and their doors faced each other : my mother had only to take a single step, and she was inside my hut. She used to do so without any warning; she never knocked at the door, she just walked straight in. Suddenly, there she would be, standing before us, without the slightest sound from the door; she would look closely at everyone before saying good evening.

Oh! it was not the faces of my men friends that she scrutinised; they were my own affair; they did not matter. No, it was the girls' faces that my mother used to inspect; and she very soon picked out the faces she did not like. I must admit that in those gatherings there were sometimes young women of rather loose habits, and whose reputation was a little tarnished. But how could I forbid them to come? Did I even want to do so? If they were a little more worldly-wise than was necessary, they were also generally the most amusing. But my mother thought otherwise, and she never used to beat about the bush.

'You,' she would say, 'what are you doing here? Your place is not with my son. Go back home. If I see you here again, I'll have something to tell your mother about you. I warn you.'

If the girl did not make off fast enough, or if she did not extract herself quickly enough from the jumble on the divan, my mother would pull her out by the arm and thrust her towards the open door.

'Go on,' she would cry, 'get back home.'

And with her hands she would pretend to be chasing away some too adventurous fowl. Only then would she say good evening to everyone.

I did not care much for this procedure, I did not care for it at all. Reports of these insults were spread abroad; and whenever I invited a girl-friend to come and visit me, she would say as often as not:

'And what if your mother catches me?'

'She won't eat you.'

'No, but she'll start shouting and show me the door.'

And I would stand there in front of the girl, wondering: 'Is there really any reason why my mother should turn her out of doors?' And I did not always know. I used to live in Conakry for the greater part of the year, and I did not know all the details of Kouroussa gossip.

But I could hardly say to the girl: 'Have people been talking about you? And if you've had any affairs, do you think my mother knows about them?' It exasperated me.

As I grew older I became more passionate; I no longer had merely half-hearted friendships – or even love affairs. I did not have only Marie or Fanta – although at first it was Marie and Fanta I had as friends. But Marie was on holiday at Bela, at her father's; and Fanta was my 'regular' girl. I respected her; and even if I had wanted to go further (and I did not want to), custom would have forbidden it. The rest . . . the rest were unimportant, but they existed nevertheless. Could my mother fail to understand the growing ardour of my blood?

She understood it only too well. Often she would get up in the middle of the night and come and make sure that I was alone in bed. She would generally make her rounds towards midnight, striking a match to light my bed. If I still happened to be awake, I would pretend to be asleep; then as if a lighted match had disturbed me, I would pretend to wake with a start.

'What's the matter?' I would cry.

'Are you asleep?' my mother would ask.

'Yes, I was asleep. Why did you keep waking me up?'

'Good, go to sleep again.'

'But how can I sleep if you wake me up?'

'Don't get worked up,' she would say. 'Go to sleep.'

But I did not care much for this kind of treatment. And I used to complain about it to Kouyaté and Check Omar, who at that time were my most intimate friends.

'Am I not old enough to look after myself?' I would ask. 'I was considered sufficiently grown-up to be given my own hut; but how can I call my hut my own if people can enter it at any hour of the day or night?'

'It shows that your mother loves you very much,'

they would answer. 'You are not going to complain of that?'

'No,' was all I could say.

But I could not help thinking that her affection for me might have been a little less exclusive and less tyrannical. And it was obvious that Check and Kouyaté enjoyed more freedom than I was allowed.

'Don't brood over it so,' Kouyaté would say. 'Play us your guitar.'

I would go and take down my guitar – Kouyaté had taught me to play. In the evening, instead of staying in my hut, we would go strolling through the streets of the town, Kouyaté and I, strumming on our guitars, while Check played the banjo and we all three sang in harmony. Girls who often were already in bed when we passed their compound would wake up and listen to us. Those who were friends of ours would recognise our voices; they would get up, dress hastily and run to join us. Though only three of us had started out, soon we would be six, and ten, and sometimes fifteen, all of us rousing the echoes in the sleeping streets.

Kouyaté and Check had been my school-fellows in the primary school at Kouroussa. They were both quick-witted and particularly gifted in mathematics. I can still remember how, when the master had barely finished dictating us a problem, they would both of them jump up and take him the finished sum. This amazing rapidity used to fill us all with wonder, but also used to fill me with discouragement, even though I always used to get my own back in French. But from that time onwards, despite – or perhaps because of this competitive spirit – we had been friends : but it was a friendship such as only very young schoolboys know – not very well founded, and impermanent.

Our real friendship did not begin in fact until after I had left our home-town to study in Conakry, and

Kouyaté and Check had left to continue their studies at, respectively, the High Schools of Popoda and Dakar. We exchanged numerous and very lengthy letters, in which we used to describe our life at school and compare notes on our lessons. Then when the holidays came we met again in Kouroussa, and we soon became inseparables.

At first our parents had not looked upon our friendship with any great favour. Either we used to disappear for whole days, forgetting meal-times and the meals themselves, or else we used to stay in the compound, so that at meal-times there would be two unexpected guests. Such behaviour was undoubtedly a little free-and-easy. But this disfavour did not last long. Our parents soon realised that if we disappeared for two out of every three days, the two guests would put in an appearance only on every third day; and they soon accepted the very fair and judicious rotation we had put into practice without consulting them.

'But couldn't you have told me?' my mother used to say. 'Couldn't you have given me notice, so that I could have prepared something special?'

'No,' I would reply. 'Our sole wish was, precisely, that no one should make any special preparations for us. All we wanted was the usual daily meal.'

In the summer holidays which came at the end of Kouyaté's and Check's third scholastic year – and at the end of my second year, since I had lost a year in hospital – I saw my two friends again; they had gained their teaching certificates and were waiting to be given posts. If their success did not surprise me, if it corresponded with everything I expected of them, nonetheless it gave me great pleasure and I congratulated them warmly. When I asked after their health, Check replied that he felt very worn-out.

'I worked hard,' he told me, 'and just at the moment

I have not quite got over it. I'm worn out.'

But was he merely 'worn out'? He looked ill and his face was drawn. A few days later I took advantage of being alone with Kouyaté a moment to ask him if he thought it was simply overwork.

'No,' Kouyaté told me. 'Check is sick. He has no appetite and he is losing weight; besides, his stomach is swelling.'

'Should we not warn him?'

'I don't know,' said Kouyaté. 'I think he's noticed it himself.'

'Isn't he doing anything for it?'

'I don't think so. He is in no pain and perhaps he thinks it will gradually get better.'

'And if it gets worse?'

We did not know what to do. We did not want to frighten Check, and yet we felt that something should really be done about it.

'I'll speak to my mother about it,' I said.

But as soon as I began to talk to her about him, she stopped me.

'Check Omar is seriously ill,' she said. 'I've been watching him for several days. I really think I should go and warn his mother.'

'Yes, do,' I said, 'because he's doing nothing about it.'

Check's mother did what was always done in the circumstances : she consulted the medicine-men. They prescribed massage and infusions. But these remedies had scarcely any effect : his stomach continued to swell, and his face looked grey. Check was not alarmed.

'I'm not in any pain,' he said. 'I haven't much appetite, but I don't feel any pain. It will probably go as quickly as it came.'

I don't know whether Check had very great confidence in the medicine-men; I rather think he had very little : we had by now spent too many years at school to have

complete faith in them. Yet our medicine-men are not
charlatans: many of them have great knowledge and
can perform real cures; and certainly Check was aware
of that. But he must have realised that this time their
remedies were not working; and that is why he said,
'It will probably go as quickly as it came,' putting
more faith in the passage of time than in massage and
infusions. His words cheered us up for a few days, then,
with brutal suddenness, they lost their comforting quality,
for Check really began to suffer. He now had violent
attacks of pain, and he used to weep in agony.

'Look,' Kouyaté told him, 'the medicine-men have
been no use to you; come with us to the dispensary!'

We went there. The doctor sounded Check and sent
him into hospital. He did not say what was wrong with
him, but now we knew that it was a serious illness, and
Check, too, knew it. Would the white doctor succeed
where our own medicine-men had failed? Evil is not
always overcome by good, and we were filled with
anxiety. We kept watch in relays at Check's bedside;
we would watch our poor friend writhing on his bed.
His stomach, swollen and hard, was cold, like something
already dead. Whenever the attacks grew worse, we
would run distractedly to the doctor: 'Doctor! Come
quickly!' But no medicine was of any use; and all we
could do was to take Check's hands in ours and press
them hard so he would not feel all alone in his pain,
and say to him, 'There, Check! . . . There! . . . Be
brave . . . it will pass.'

All week we stayed at his bedside: his mother, his
brothers, my mother and the mother of Kouyaté. Then,
towards the end of the week, Check suddenly ceased to
suffer, and we told the others to go and rest. Check
was now sleeping peacefully, and we did not dare to
awaken him. We watched him sleeping, and a great
hope began to spring in our hearts. His face had grown

so thin that all the bones stood out, but his features were
no longer drawn, and his lips seemed to be smiling. Then
gradually the pain came back, the lips ceased to smile,
and Check woke up. He began by dictating to us his
last wishes. He told us how we should share out his
books and to whom we should give his banjo. His voice
was now getting fainter and fainter, and we could not
always catch the end of his words. Then he said good-
bye to us once again. When he stopped speaking, it was
not far off midnight. Then as the dispensary clock
finished the twelve strokes, he died . . .

I feel as if I were living through those days and nights
again, and I do not believe I have ever spent more
wretched ones. I wandered aimlessly here and there;
we both, Kouyaté and myself, wandered around as if
we had lost our wits, our thoughts full of Check. To
have lived so many happy days . . . and then for everything to be over! 'Check . . .' I kept saying to myself; we both kept saying it to ourselves; and we had to
restrain ourselves from saying his name out loud. But
his shade, his shade alone accompanied us. And when
we managed to get things a little clearer in our minds –
and we could not see things too clearly – we saw him in
the centre of his compound, laid out on a bier, laid out
under his winding-sheet, ready to be laid in the earth;
or it was in the earth itself, laid out, at the bottom of his
grave, his head raised a little, waiting for the covering
of planks to be placed over him, then the leaves, the
great mounds of leaves, and finally the earth itself, so
dark, and so heavy.

'Check! . . . Check! . . .' But I could not say his
name aloud: you must never lift up your voice to address
the dead. And yet, at night, it was almost as if I *had*
lifted up my voice to speak with the dead: suddenly,
he would be standing before me. And I would wake
up, my body bathed in sweat; I would be seized with

fear, for, if we loved Check's ghostly shade, if his shade was all that was left to us, we feared it almost as much as we loved it, and we no longer dared sleep alone, we no longer dared to face our dreams alone . . .

Whenever I think today of those distant times, I hardly know just what it was I was so frightened of. But that is probably because I no longer look upon death as I used to : I look upon it much more simply. I think of those past days, and now quite simply I think that Check has gone before us along God's highway, and that all of us will one day walk along that highway, which is no more frightening than the other . . . The other? . . . Yes, the other : the highway of life, the one we set foot on when we are born, and which is only the highway of our momentary exile.

Twelve

WHEN I went back to Kouroussa with my proficiency certificate in my pocket, and feeling, I must confess, a little swollen-headed by my success, I was of course received with open arms, just as I had been received at the end of every scholastic year, with the same eagerness, the same warm affection. This year, a fresh sense of pride was there. On the road from the station to our compound, there had been the most enthusiastic demonstrations to welcome me, and they had all sprung from the same love, the same friendship. But even as my parents pressed me to their breasts, my mother perhaps rejoicing more at my return than at the diploma I had won, my mind was uneasy, especially as regards my mother.

This was because before leaving Conakry the head of

the school had sent for me and had asked me if I would like to go to France to complete my studies. I had blithely answered yes, but I had said it without consulting my parents, without having consulted my mother. My uncles in Conakry had told me that it was a unique opportunity, and that I did not deserve to live if I turned it down. What would my parents say? Particularly my mother? I did not feel at all comfortable. I waited until the ecstatic greeting had died down a little, and then I exclaimed, as if the news would be a source of delight to everyone:

'And that's not all: the headmaster wants to send me to France!'

'To France?' said my mother.

I saw her face contract.

'Yes, I shall be given a scholarship. It will not cost you anything.'

'As if the cost mattered,' said my mother. 'Do you mean to say you're going to leave us again?'

'Well, I don't know yet.'

I could see what I had already feared, that I had been rather too hasty and imprudent in saying 'Yes' to the headmaster.

'You're not going,' said my mother.

'No,' I said. 'But it would not be for longer than a year.'

'A year?' said my father. 'A year, that's not so very long.'

'What?' my mother broke in sharply. 'A year isn't so very long? For the last four years our son has hardly ever been with us except for the holidays, and you can stand there and say a year is not so very long?'

'Oh, well . . .' my father began.

'No, no,' my mother cried, 'our son is not going. Let that be the end of the matter.'

'All right,' said my father, 'we won't mention it

again. For this day is the day of his return, the day of his success. Let us rejoice. We'll talk about the other thing later on.'

We said no more about it, for people were beginning to crowd into the compound, eager to celebrate my return.

Late that night, when everyone was in bed, I went and sat beside my father under the veranda of his hut. The headmaster had said that he required my father's official consent before he could do anything, and that this consent should reach him with the shortest delay.

'My father,' I said, 'when the headmaster asked me if I would like to go to France, I said yes.'

'Ah! You've already accepted?'

'I couldn't help saying yes. I didn't think what I was saying at the time, or what you and my mother would think.'

'Do you really want to go there?' he asked.

'Yes,' I said. 'My Uncle Mamadou told me that it was a unique opportunity.'

'You could have gone to Dakar. Your Uncle Mamadou went to Dakar.'

'It wouldn't be the same thing.'

'No, it would not be the same thing. But how are you going to break it to your mother?'

'Then do you agree to my departure?' I cried.

'Yes . . . Yes, I'm willing. Because of you. But do you hear, it's because of you I'm doing it, for your own good.'

And he was silent a while.

'You see,' he said, 'it's something I've often thought about. I've thought about it in the silence of the night and in the clangour of the forge. I knew quite well that one day you would leave us. I knew it the very first day you set foot in school. I watched you studying with such eagerness, such passionate eagerness! . . . Yes, since that day, I knew how it would be: and gradually I resigned myself to it.'

'Father!' I said.

'Each one follows his own destiny, my son. Men can do nothing to change it. This opportunity is within your reach: you must seize it. You've already seized one, seize this one too, make sure of it. There are still so many things to be done in our land . . . Yes, I want you to go to France; I want that now, just as much as you do. Soon we'll be needing men here like you . . . Maybe you'll not be gone too long!'

We sat for a long time without saying anything under the veranda, looking out into the night. Then suddenly my father said in a broken voice:

'Promise me that you will come back?'

'I shall come back,' I said.

'These distant lands . . .' he whispered slowly.

He left the phrase unfinished: he went on looking out into the darkness. I could see him, by the light of the storm-lantern, looking out into the night as if at a fixed point, and frowning as if he was dissatisfied or uneasy at what he saw there.

'What are you looking at?' I asked.

'Beware of ever deceiving anyone,' he said. 'Be upright in thought and deed. And God shall be with you.'

Then he made what seemed a gesture of despair, and turned his eyes away from the darkness.

The next day, I wrote to the headmaster that my father had given his permission. And I kept it a secret from everyone; I confided only in Kouyaté. Then I began travelling round the district. I could go anywhere

I liked; I visited the nearby towns; I went to Kankan, which is our holy city. When I came back, my father showed me the letter that the headmaster of the Technical College had sent him. The headmaster confirmed my departure and named the French school where I was to study : the school was at Argenteuil.

'Do you know where Argenteuil is?' asked my father.

'No,' I said, 'I'll go and have a look.'

I went and looked it up in my dictionary and I saw that Argenteuil was only a few miles from Paris.

'It's near Paris,' I said.

And I began dreaming about Paris! Then my thoughts returned suddenly to my mother.

'Have you told my mother yet?' I asked.

'No,' he replied. 'We'll go together and give her the news.'

'You wouldn't like to tell her yourself?'

'By myself? No, my son. Believe me, even if both of us go, we'll be outnumbered.'

And we began to look for my mother. We found her crushing millet for the evening meal. My father stood a long while watching the pestle rising and falling in the mortar. He hardly knew where to begin. He knew that the decision he had to make would hurt my mother and he himself had a heavy heart. He stood there watching the pestle and saying nothing; and I dared not lift my eyes. But my mother did not take long to guess what was in the wind. She only had to look at us in order to understand everything, or almost everything.

'What do you want?' she said. 'Can't you see I'm busy.'

And she began pounding faster and faster.

'Don't go so fast,' my father said, 'you'll wear yourself out.'

'Are you trying to teach me how to pound millet?' she said.

And then all of a sudden she went on angrily:

'If you want to discuss our son's departure for France, you can save your breath. He's not going.'

'That's just it,' said my father, 'you don't know what you're talking about. You do not realise what such an opportunity means to him.'

'I don't want to know,' she said.

Suddenly she dropped the pestle and took a few steps towards us.

'Shall I never have peace of mind?' she cried. 'Yesterday, it was the school at Conakry; today, it's a school in France; tomorrow . . . what will it be next? Every day there's some mad scheme to take my son away from me! . . . Have you already forgotten how sick he was at Conakry? But that's not enough for you: now you want to send him to France! Are you crazy? Or do you want to send me out of my mind? I'll certainly end up raving mad . . . And as for you,' she cried, turning towards me, 'you are nothing but an ungrateful son. Any excuse is good enough for you to run away from your mother. But this time it won't be as *you* want: you'll stop right here. Your place is here. What *are* they thinking about, at the school? Do they imagine I'm going to live my whole life apart from my son? Die with him far away? Have they no mothers, those people? But they can't have mothers, of course. They would not have gone so far away from home if they'd had mothers.'

And she lifted up her eyes to the sky, and addressed the heavens:

'Would you let them do that? Have you no heart?' she said. 'And now they want to take him away to their own land! . . .'

Then she lowered her gaze and looked at my father again.

'He's been away from me so many years already!'

'Woman! Woman!' said my father. 'Don't you know it's for his own good?'

'His own good? The best thing for him is to stay here with us. Hasn't he learnt enough already?'

'Mother,' I began.

But she turned on me violently.

'You be quiet. You're still just a little boy, a nobody. What do you want to go so far away for? Do you so much as know how people live out there? . . . No, you don't know anything about it. And tell me this, who's going to look after you? Who's going to mend your clothes? Who'll cook for you?'

'Come, come,' said my father, 'be reasonable. The White Men don't die of hunger.'

'So you haven't realized, you poor crazy thing, you haven't noticed that they don't eat as we do? This child will fall sick; that's what will happen. And then what will I do? What will become of me? Oh, I once had a son, but now I have a son no more!'

I went up to her and pressed her to me.

'Get away from me,' she shouted. 'You're no son of mine.'

But she did not push me away; she was weeping and she held me closely to her.

'You won't leave me alone, will you? Tell me you won't leave me alone.'

But now she knew that I would go away and that she could not stop my departure, that nothing could stop it. Perhaps she had known it from the first. Yes, she must have guessed at the workings of the inner wheels which, from the school in Kouroussa, led me to Conakry and would finally take me to France; and all the time she had been talking and fighting against it, she must have been watching the wheels going round and round: first this wheel, then that one, and then this third and greater wheel, then still more wheels, many more wheels perhaps, that no one else could see. And how could their working be stopped? We could only watch them turning and turning, watch the wheels of destiny turning and turning: my destiny was to go away from home. And my mother began to direct her anger against those who, to her mind, were taking me away from her once again. But already they were only useless shreds of anger.

'Those people are never satisfied,' she said. 'They want to have everything. As soon as they set eyes on a thing, they want it for themselves.'

'You must not malign them,' I replied.

'No,' she said bitterly, 'I shall not malign them.'

And finally she found that her anger and her rage were spent. She laid her head on my shoulder and wept noisily. My father had crept away. And I held her close. I dried her tears, I said . . . what did I say to her? Everything, and anything that came into my head, but nothing was of any importance. I don't think my mother understood a word of what I was saying; all she was aware of was the sound of my voice. And that was enough. Her sobs gradually grew quieter and less frequent . . .

That was how my departure was arranged. And so one day I stepped on a plane for France. Oh! it was a terrible parting! I do not like to think of it. I can still hear my mother's wailing, I can still see my father, unable to hide his tears, I can still see my sisters, my brothers. . . . No, I do not like to remember that parting. It was as if I was being torn apart.

In Conakry, the headmaster told me that the plane would land at Orly.

'From Orly,' he said, 'you will be taken to Paris,

to the Invalides station. There you will take the Métro to St Lazare station, where you will find the train for Argenteuil.'

He unfolded a Métro map and showed me the route I should be taking in the depths of the earth. But the map meant nothing to me, and the very idea of travelling underground was extremely vague to me.

'Are you sure you understand?' the headmaster asked me.

'Yes,' I said.

But I did not quite understand everything.

'Take the map with you.'

I slipped it into my pocket. The headmaster looked at me.

'You're not overdressed,' he said.

I was wearing white cotton trousers and an open-necked sports shirt, sleeveless; on my feet I was wearing sandals and white socks.

'You'll have to wear more over there. At this time of the year, it's already beginning to get colder.'

I left for the airport with Marie and my uncles; Marie was going with me as far as Dakar, where she was to continue her studies. Marie . . . I got into the plane with her. I was crying; we were all crying. Then the propeller began to turn. In the distance, my uncles were waving to us for the last time. And the earth, the land of Guinea, began to drop rapidly away.

'Are you glad to be going?' Marie asked me when the plane was nearing Dakar.

'I don't know,' I answered. 'I don't think so.'

And when the plane landed at Dakar, Marie said to me :

'Will you be coming back?'

Her face was wet with tears.

'Yes,' I said, 'yes . . .'

And nodded in the affirmative again as I fell back,

right back in my seat, for I did not want anyone to see my tears. Surely I would be coming back! I sat a long while without moving, my arms folded, tightly folded, to stifle the heaving of my breast.

Later on, I felt something hard when I put my hand in my pocket. It was the map of the Métro . . .

Fontana Paperbacks

Fontana is a leading paperback publisher of fiction and non-fiction, with authors ranging from Alistair MacLean, Agatha Christie and Desmond Bagley to Solzhenitsyn and Pasternak, from Gerald Durrell and Joy Adamson to the famous Modern Masters series.

In addition to a wide-ranging collection of internationally popular writers of fiction, Fontana also has an outstanding reputation for history, natural history, military history, psychology, psychiatry, politics, economics, religion and the social sciences.

All Fontana books are available at your bookshop or newsagent; or can be ordered direct. Just fill in the form and list the titles you want.

FONTANA BOOKS, Cash Sales Department, G.P.O. Box 29, Douglas, Isle of Man, British Isles. Please send purchase price, plus 8p per book. Customers outside the U.K. send purchase price, plus 10p per book. Cheque, postal or money order. No currency.

NAME (Block letters) _____

ADDRESS _____

_____

_____
